Change, Hope, and the Bomb

Change, Hope, and The Bomb

By David E. Lilienthal

PRINCETON, NEW JERSEY

PRINCETON UNIVERSITY PRESS

1963

Printed in the United States of America
by Princeton University Press, Princeton, New Jersey

Second Printing 1963

TO MY SON

AUTHOR'S NOTE

I N F E B R U A R Y 1963 I gave the Stafford Little
Lecture series at Princeton University. This book is
based on the theme of those lectures, but I have made
substantial revisions, in the form and by the addition
of material and subjects not part of the lectures as
delivered.

I am in debt to a great many people—too numerous
to name—for the opportunity they gave me to discuss
with them and to test my ideas about the Atom, in
the years since Hiroshima.

In the many months of writing this book I have en-
joyed and greatly benefited by the mature critical judgment and extensive editorial assistance of my son
David. Parts of the manuscript were critically read by
Joseph Volpe Jr., former General Counsel of the
Atomic Energy Commission and now a practicing
lawyer in Washington, D.C., to whom I wish to
express special thanks for his candor and helpful-
ness. I am deeply indebted to the late Gordon R.
Clapp, friend and fellow-worker of mine for over
twenty-five years, for the encouragement and insights
he provided me. My wife Helen's unfailing patience
and forbearance as well as her editorial aid helped
more than I can say as I worked my way through the
problems of analysis and writing while at the same
time carrying heavy business responsibilities. Finally

AUTHOR'S NOTE

I wish to convey my thanks to Mildred Baron and Anne Stebbins for their skilled and indefatigable secretarial assistance in getting the lectures and then this book through many revisions to a final form.

One Whitehall Street
New York City
June 18, 1963

CONTENTS

Change, Hope, and the Bomb

A PERSONAL FOREWORD

O N T H E fifteenth of February in 1950 I walked out of my office, the office of the Chairman of the Atomic Energy Commission, down the marble stairs, and handed my security badge to the officer at the door for the last time. I was once more a private citizen. For the first time in years an official responsibility for the split Atom was off my shoulders. I said to myself: "Now, I've finally left the Atom behind, for someone else to worry about."

But I found I couldn't leave the Atom behind. It continued to be a part of my life as a private individual, as it is a part of the life of every reader of these words, as it is an inseparable part of the life and destiny of every human being.

This is a book about the Atom, but it is also a personal testament. A book on so pervasive a subject as the Atom inevitably has a personal setting. It is necessarily a reflection of how the writer sees the world, a projection of his own special and unique experience of life applied to the gravest problems men have faced in many generations.

More specifically, this book about the Atom is an affirmation of what my own experience of life tells me about how men get things done, not in the theories and abstractions that are found in books, but in real life.

3

And so, before discussing such specific aspects of the Atom as our policy about nuclear weapons, disarmament, peaceful energy from the Atom, the changing role of scientists, and so on, I should state my basic personal outlook.

I am a hopeful and an optimistic man. But I am not hopeful and sanguine for learned or technical or doctrinaire reasons. I cannot and will not try in this book to prove by abstract reasoning why I am hopeful. Indeed, the kind of work in which my life has been spent makes it difficult for me to understand or follow—or be persuaded by—abstract and oh-so-logical analysis of the atomic predicament. Nor do I have any confidence in doctrinaire "blueprints" for survival, or a plan that tells humankind just what it must do to be saved. To me it is not that kind of world; man is not built for blueprints, Great Plans, or Final Solutions.

Hopefulness and optimism are a part of my testament of faith because man must have hope if he is to be a man. And hope there is.

In this book I shall seek to describe the multiple, diverse, and unpredictable sources of that hope in a world confronted with the atomic dilemma. But the foundation on which hope is built is not subject to proof in a mathematical or scientific sense, nor can it be set out in a formula or a political program. For to say, as has been so often said since the advent of nuclear arms and long before, that there is one road

4

to peace, or to salvation, or to prosperity or tranquility is to deny the wisdom of all history and to contravert all human experience.

Because there is no one formula to put the world to rights does not mean that we do not keep trying to do so, step by step. It does mean that we must rely on the hopefulness that lies in change, unpredictable change. Seizing on these changes rather than looking for one new single panacea or doctrine or program or plan, is what makes life so invigorating and so hopeful.

The foundation of my outlook on life, reflected in the views about the Atom expressed in this book, is a confidence, even a reverence, for the capacities of man. A thousand books by a thousand learned soothsayers of our Fluent Society are not as meaningful to me as what I have seen at first hand of what men can do, and what in many cases I have worked along with them to do.

Seeing what men are capable of I have come to stand in awe of man's creative potentialities. This sense of awe began early in my life. In my early thirties I committed myself to work with the people in the Valley of the Tennessee. The whole country was in a Depression, but in that Valley most of its people had never known anything else. The rest of the country looked down upon the South and the capacities of its people; but the spirit of those people with whom I worked day in and day out burst into a flame of confidence in themselves, and they transformed their Valley within a decade. Those people today, after thirty years, sense no limitation on what they can do. They know that they can somehow do what needs to be done.

Seven years ago I began to work with the people of a vast region of Iran. The actual rulers of that region were the owners of land; the tillers of the land were nothing—they were thought to be dispirited and hopelessly defeated by centuries of half-animal existence. As I write, those same peasants are taking over the land from landowners; it is these peasants who will finally rebuild the agricultural sinews of a region that was green and fertile in the ancient days when it was the center of power of the great Persian Empire. When I first saw it only seven years ago it seemed a hopeless desert; today it is again becoming green and productive. I have seen the light come back into the eyes of the Iranian tillers of the soil; one remembers that before centuries of submergence their forbears were rulers of a world empire. Sophisticated people judged these peasants to be of no account, helpless, doomed to unproductive poverty. They underestimated the life force, the indomitable power of men.

Not so many years ago I worked in the south of Italy and the islands of Sicily and Sardinia. The sophisticates had written these people off, too, for centuries. They said that the only remedy for southern Italy was for the southern Italians to leave. But again the in-

6

tellectuals had too little faith in man when he is aroused. All of Italy forges ahead these days as it has not since Roman times, and the greatest resource of Italy turns out to be Italians—of whom there aren't enough.

A life spent, as mine has been, with men who are doing specific things against desperate odds leaves its mark on a man. It does not make him a Pollyanna; I have seen and lived through my share of setbacks, crises, disappointments, cruelty and viciousness. All is not sweetness and light; progress is not inevitable. But one who has seen the incalculable power of men fired with purpose, can never feel that human affairs are hopeless.

There is another aspect of my particular experience of life that ought to be set down. In the course of observing *what* men have done, I have had a chance to observe and reflect upon *how* they get things done. I have found it is by what I call the technique of the manageable job, in short the art of achieving the possible, and thereby of bringing the impossible progressively closer to our grasp. This process of the manageable job is directly relevant to my own view of how we can meet the threat of the Atom.

This concept of the manageable job is an approach to human affairs that is hopeful and affirmative, for it stimulates the creative powers of men by demonstrating, case by case, what *can* be done. This is the underlying theme of this book: what sort of moves toward peace in the world are not now manageable; what sort are manageable. The manageable job, as a guide to action, is not that of seeking some single, final solution. It is rather the far more arduous and earthy one of seizing the many opportunities to act which constant change in the world offers, and thereby gradually bringing within the reach of human management the fearful Atom that threatens us all.

CHAPTER I

———◦○◦———

THE IMPERATIVES OF
CHANGE

IN THE WHOLE of history, no single force has cast a greater terror over all mankind than the Atom. Since Hiroshima, the image of final catastrophe has seized on the minds and hearts of men. The Atom has so heightened the desperate problems of a world in turmoil that it seems to have fused them all together into one single universal issue: can an atomic holocaust somehow be avoided?

We have become possessed by our fear. In our efforts to find ways of coping with the threat of the Atom, we have concentrated almost exclusively on the Atom itself. We may from time to time remind ourselves that the problem of the Atom is essentially an intensification of the age-old human problem of managing to live peacefully on earth, but in fact our approach to the Atom has been largely influenced by our fascinated terror of the Bomb. We have tended to regard it as if it were something outside humanity, a satanic power that dominates the affairs of men without actually being part of them.

The purpose of this book is to take a fresh look at the Atom, to see if there is not a new approach, a new outlook, that may help us toward a broader understanding—and toward hope.

But I do not believe that any approach can be new or fruitful if it is rooted in the assumption that the Atom is a thing apart from the life of mankind. My conviction is that there is no Atomic Issue; rather, there are Human Issues, and therefore we must look not narrowly at the Atom alone but at the Atom as it is a part of the world today.

For this reason, therefore, before proceeding to reexamine the Human Issues of the Atom, I think it is important to take a broad view of what is bigger than the Atom and of which the Atom is an important part, but only a part: the world of men and of nations today. What kind of a world is it?

It is a world of change—swift, radical change—change at a tempo unprecedented in history. It is a world of creativity: of new ideas, new ambitions, new cruelties and new compassions, a world where outworn ideas are being discarded. A world in transformation.

It is a world of men who are uniting here, separating there—quarrelling, fighting, rebelling, building—but constantly on the move toward something different.

It is a world that is fluid and exciting. Of evil and violence there is plenty; of standing still there is little. Movement and change of a scale and intensity never before known: this is the world of today.

10

From the day in 1950 when I left my official pre-occupation with the Atom, my work as a private citizen has enabled me to observe or take part in remarkable changes in many areas of the world. In Latin America and Asia I have seen evidence of perhaps the greatest migration of human beings in history, the tidal movement of people from the land to the cities. I have seen vast social changes: the ancient power of the great landlords weakened beyond restoration in the south of Italy and in parts of the Middle East and elsewhere in Asia. I have seen vast physical changes wrought by men: new cities built, deserts made green and fruitful, great rivers put in harness.

As a layman I have caught the excitement in the community of scientists from new concepts and discoveries in physics, in biology, in medicine, in mathematics. And of course, with everyone else, I have been made daily aware of political changes: the birth of new nations, the rapid shifting of alignments and loyalties, the ferment of hostilities in the Middle East and Africa on the one hand and the growth of a powerful interdependent European community on the other.

What I have witnessed—what we all have witnessed —is the working of human desires. Not the Atom, not science, not ideology but man is the source of change, the source of power in the world. Man's fears and hopes, his passions and his resolve—these are the dominant forces, now as always.

11

This is the setting in which I propose to look at the broad human issues that are bound up in the Atom: the world of human affairs, a world in constant change under the imperative force of man's will and his heart.

CHAPTER II

THE SOLUTION FALLACY

BOUNDLESS CHANGE, individual restlessness and movement and creativity, the surge of new ideas and new energies—this is the world of 1963. Yet over this world there hangs what the President has called the Nuclear Sword of Damocles.

Here, in that part of the world scene which we call the Atom, the dominant mood is not of daring, not affirmation, not change and challenge. The mood is negative: fear, anxiety, a monumental sense of frustration in which the only hope is a static one, a hope of sheer survival.

With the Atom, time is suspended. The bombs have grown bigger and far more numerous, and the daily confrontation of antagonist nuclear forces therefore more terrifying. But I do not see that there has been any essential change in thinking about the Atom since the end of World War II—change of the kind that, for good or bad, has revolutionized so many other areas of human activity.

First we had the bomb, and then—rather quickly— the Russians had it, too. And so we produced a super-bomb, a thermo-nuclear bomb: the Russians were not slow to respond with their own super-bombs. As E. B.

White puts it: "Bomb begets bomb. A begets H. Anything you can build I can build bigger." And so the story has gone.

The story of nuclear weapons is not one of change in a world of change, but essentially one of repetition—a circle in which we and the Russians have gone round and round, chasing each others' tails, year after year after year. This is the source of our despair, of our frustration, of our fear. We seem to remain locked in the same cell of circumstance, the Russians and ourselves together, with what at times seems only a remote hope of ever emerging.

Over the years we have gone from one frustration to another, each failure feeding the mood of pessimism and despair. The threat of annihilation has increased, while a solid hope of removing that threat or of reducing its imminence seems to have dwindled to insignificance.

It is time now to take a new hard look at the atomic policies we have followed since Hiroshima. Those policies have not succeeded; there can be little argument about that. The important question is whether they have represented the only courses of action open to us.

I do not believe that they have. I believe that we can and must find a fresh approach, a different perspective. One of the first steps, surely, toward such a new outlook is for us—and the world—to look for the sources of our failure, and then to jettison whatever

14

outmoded and illusory ideas we find we are still following.

Until recently a challenge to any of our basic assumptions about the Atom would have been futile even to propound. The basic assumptions about nuclear weapons beginning with Hiroshima in 1945 and continuing until perhaps the death of Secretary Dulles were so deeply ingrained in the thinking and the emotions of many public officials and of the public at large that even to raise questions would have brought down upon oneself a cloud of recrimination; no serious thinking would result.

In 1950, for example, those of us in the Government who called for a re-examination of the then basic assumption that we needed virtually no strong conventional arms but only bigger nuclear weapons—the H-bomb—found this question to be a wholly futile exercise in the atmosphere of that frenetic time. Far from opening the minds of men and causing them to think and examine their assumptions afresh, these questions actually tended to freeze the prevailing mental and emotional attitudes and force acceptance of the doctrine that a super-bomb could be a sole guarantee for our military security.

Today the doctrine is in a different form: that the only hope is for redoubled efforts for a negotiated reduction and then abolition of armaments with Russia. In circles that are influential, and utterly dedicated and sincere, this has become almost an article of faith

15

in our country. Yet it has happened before that the hard facts have forced into discard an article of faith almost sacred in the catalogue of our convictions; then a new understanding, a new perspective, has emerged.

Let me refer only to one case in relatively recent American history: the death of isolationism as a basic philosophy of American political life.

The theme of isolation from the affairs of Europe runs through the entire history of the United States. It became an assumption not subject to serious question. Almost up to the beginning of World War II, only a tiny minority believed that we should draw closer to Europe or have a hand in European affairs. But changed facts buried that doctrine of isolationism and buried it deep. What to one generation or one decade is permanent and unchangeable, turns out to be not permanent and immutable at all when it collides with new facts—in this case the facts that the Atlantic Ocean no longer was a protection to the United States and that trade and alliance with Europe were essential to our strength and security.

The death of isolationism as an American political theology is but one instance that beliefs so firmly ingrained as to appear beyond challenge are indeed subject to the imperative of change. These beliefs *will* become weakened if their pursuit proves to be futile and frustrating, or if the facts that support them are supplanted by others.

16

That is why I now feel that perhaps for the first time since 1950 there is point in my speaking my mind on the subject of nuclear weapons.

The atmosphere, the climate of emotion, the impulse to punish those who differ, and the cocksureness in the minds of men have begun to moderate. This difference is not because of technical changes but because of facts long known to men generally, facts about the limitations of man that cannot be overlooked, facts which now so plainly demand that some of the assumptions about atomic weapons be challenged, examined, reappraised.

Atomic energy was the product of many different kinds of specialized knowledge. Its achievement represents a very high order of imagination and creativity indeed, but it is also a high point in the fragmentation of knowledge and of responsibility for knowledge. So complex an achievement as atomic energy, with so many ramifications, coming so suddenly and under circumstances that required secrecy, required a high degree of compartmentalization. The scientific—the technological—the military—the diplomatic—the political—even the grave ethical implications were customarily dealt with as separate kinds of expertise. The technicians and experts and specialists took over the Atom. They took it over in pieces, not as a whole. To this day no one has ever been able—or tried very hard, I think—to put the pieces together in an over-all way. The preoccupation has been with bits and pieces.

17

In such a circumstance alienation from the fabric of the rest of life was inevitable. That alienation now is almost complete.

The place of the Atom in the life of the world cannot be understood, much less dealt with creatively in its military as well as its non-military aspects so long as we continue to think of it as the exclusive domain of the experts, fragmented and compartmentalized into a score or more fields of expertise. The basis for understanding atomic energy in the life of mankind is not the mastery of physics or abstract mathematics or diplomacy or military science or the exotic nuances of some disarmament plan. To understand the Atom we must reassert what through the ages men have come painfully to know of the condition of man in a changing world, how human affairs are conducted—and misconducted.

The Atom has had us bewitched. It was so gigantic, so terrible, so beyond the power of imagination to embrace, that it seemed to be the ultimate fact. It would either destroy us all or it would bring about the millennium. It was the final secret of Nature, greater by far than man himself, and it was, it seemed, invulnerable to the ordinary processes of life, the processes of growth, decay, change. Our obsession with the Atom led us to assign to it a separate and unique status in the world. So greatly did it seem to transcend the ordinary affairs of men that we shut it out of those

18

affairs altogether; or rather, tried to create a separate world, a world of the Atom.

Doing this, it seems to me, we forgot what we all really know: that if we are to be destroyed, or if some version of the millennium is to be created, man and man alone will be the destroyer or creator, as he has always been. It is still man that counts. Man, always changing, renewing himself from generation to generation, is never obsolete.

Man is never obsolete—but particular groups of men may be, if they cling too long to ideas and outlooks which the imperatives of a changing world demand to be discarded.

To most of our atomic ideas, inherited almost intact and unchanged from another epoch, the words of President Kennedy at Yale in the spring of 1962 have a terrible relevance: "Mythology distracts us everywhere . . . we must move on," he said—about economics, but with even greater pertinence to our outlook on the Atom. "We must move on from the reassuring repetition of stale phrases to a new, difficult but essential confrontation with reality."

My object now is to examine our beliefs in the light of what I conceive to be the condition of the world today—to separate, if possible, mythology from reality.

Our policies and programs about the Atom have changed over the years since Hiroshima, but they all have stemmed from the same general outlook, a point of view powerfully rooted in our emotions. This has given our course of policy a consistency—a terrible, tragic consistency—leading us step by step into our present dilemma.

We have been following a myth. We have been committed to an illusion about the Atom which has forced us year by year to attempt to make the facts of life fit a concept, instead of trying to frame policies and programs that will fit the facts.

What is the essence of this myth? To my mind, it is this: That because the development of the Atomic Bomb seemed to be the ultimate breakthrough in scientific achievement, in the control of physical matter, we could make a similarly radical departure in dealing with those problems in human affairs which the Bomb so greatly intensified. The Bomb was so colossal, a new force in the world, that we believed a new way must be found to meet its threat, an approach similarly sweeping, similarly radical and world-wide.

In short, our obsession with the Atom drove us to seek a Grand Solution. We became committed to the concept of a total final settlement because nothing short of this would answer the tremendous threat.

Therefore we tried and have continued to try to deal with the Atom by inventing a new set of rules. We set aside everything the human race had previously learned about man's behavior, about war and peace, about the way human institutions work, about the conditions that govern the course of men and nations in a diverse and changing world.

20

In our own experience in America we have come painfully to a kind of national maturity through an incredibly complex and constantly changing series of adjustments. Our institutions and our society could not have survived the impacts of technological revolutions, of the great migrations and movements of peoples, of depressions and wars, if they were not capable of absorbing and accommodating all of these various and often contradictory pulls of change. What we have achieved is a nation of multiple interests, multiple opportunities. No single phrase can describe America. We are not Socialist, and yet government is the most powerful and dominant of our institutions. We have left behind the root ideas of traditional Capitalism (as seen by Marx and others), and yet the life of our society depends on the workings of private initiative and private money. We are justly proud of our practicality, of our distrust of dogmas and certainties. We are not a nation of theorists but a nation of doers. And if there is any single national characteristic that we ought to prize, it is a skepticism that goes hand in hand with tolerance.

It is not strange that the upsetting of experts frequently warms our hearts. Why? Because, I think, it confirms our innate sense of our own worth, of our power to create and shape events, of our existence as diverse sentient beings whose future cannot be measured by the scientist and the engineer or laid

21

down in graphs by the sociologist or economist. We are not inanimate objects, but men.

And so we are—or we ought to be—skeptical of anyone who comes up with an Answer with a capital A, whether it is the forecast of doom or the promise of plenty. The failure of an agreement on a particular plan for disarmament at Geneva, for example, does not dismay me, because I have come to have faith in the incredibly varied, fantastically fluid, enormously complex and unpredictable movements of change all over the world, in a thousand places and in a thousand of the activities of men, and I do not believe that all can be lost, or won, by one little group of men sitting at a conference table.

We have, as a people, learned pretty well how to separate rhetoric and reality. We are willing to try out new ideas and new methods, but we have an instinctive reaction against anything that promises the millennium or threatens us with the End of Everything overnight. We know that things just don't work that way in our country, or in the world.

We know because we have tried some Grand Solutions ourselves. We tried to eliminate the misuse of liquor by abolishing liquor through Prohibition. We tried to solve our problems with other nations by denying that they existed, through Isolationism. Every time, the illusion has been battered down by the facts, and in the process we have learned more about ourselves, about what can be done and about what can't.

22

However, it is not hard to understand why we rejected the lessons of our own national history and seized on the idea that the Atom could be "solved," for once and all. The Atom seemed to present a whole new order of problems. It appeared to supersede and take precedence over every aspect of life that it touched, so that the grave problems of military and foreign policy and human relations were essentially transformed into a single monolithic problem: the Atom.

The very suddenness of the Atom's appearance contributed to this conception. We know that the advent of electricity has altered our entire way of life, that the automotive engine has brought a revolution to our society, that the electron has transformed our whole scheme of communications, and with it, our culture. And yet in these and similar cases the discoveries of science did not pose a terrible and immediate threat, but came upon us gradually, and so were adapted and incorporated into the whole fabric of our lives. It was not so with the Atom.

We became obsessed with the idea of a Single Solution for the Atom because we were obsessed with the revolutionary destructive power of the Atom itself. We became emotionally committed to the search for an Answer because we felt there *had* to be one.

My own first involvement with the Atom was a part of the beginnings of this search for some Answer, some means of controlling this terrible new source of destructive energy.

This was in the first months of 1946. The United States, with the United Kingdom and Canada, had committed itself to international control of the Atom. I was made chairman of a five-man board of consultants to the State Department, consisting of Robert Oppenheimer, Charles A. Thomas, Chester I. Barnard, Harry A. Winne, and myself. With political commitment for international control as our charter we were charged with the task of taking a look at all of the relevant facts about the Atom, as they were at that time, and we were asked to develop the groundwork for an American proposal for international control.

The proposals we advanced were not solely preoccupied with weapons. We concluded early in our discussions that a purely negative approach of banning weapons and trying to establish a world-wide police-like inspection system would be unworkable. We agreed that we must base our proposals on the positive possibilities of atomic energy by invoking the principle of cooperative development of its peaceful applications, as part of an evolving system of protection against its destructive aspects.

These ideas of ours were later embodied in the official American proposal, the Baruch Plan. The program itself, of course, is dead; the situation has completely changed since that day when America alone had the Bomb and the wartime alliance with the Soviet Union against the defeated Axis had not crumbled.

Our Board of Consultants' proposal had strong support from the scientific community and also from much of the American public and Congress. It is interesting to recall, however, that back in 1946 our proposal was criticized in some circles *not* because it was too grandiose or sweeping, but because it was not sweeping enough. Some critics complained that we left too many questions unanswered, too many contingencies unprovided for—and that we had done so deliberately, which was true, for I had stated that we regarded our proposal "a place to begin, a foundation on which to build."

We felt in 1946 that a program looking toward international development and control of atomic energy did have a reasonable chance, but we also felt that neither we nor any group of men could possibly have the prescience to devise a plan that could be anything more than "a place to begin." We did not feel there could be a pat, explicit Answer; rather, from our own varied experience we Board members knew that a workable system of control would need to grow and develop over a period of many years, gradually reaching out from one achieved possibility to another.

So we viewed with some dismay those modifications of our thesis that the proposal should be only "a place to begin"; we felt it unwise to extend the scope to include at the outset too many of the issues that would later arise, that these could be better comprehended and resolved as the plan evolved.

The Baruch Plan, though it gained wide support in the world, was doomed by the unwillingness of the Russians to negotiate along these lines. They were obsessed by the knowledge that we had the Bomb while they did not; and as the long months of that lost and tragic time passed, their obsession with the fact of the Bomb became ours, too.

That obsession became a fundamental article of faith with many Americans, the faith that there was, somewhere, just around the corner, a Single Solution to the host of human problems that are bound up with the Atom, that there was a way to put the genie back in the bottle.

And, following this fundamental belief, the search went on for this Single Solution of the Atom *in one area and one area only*, the area of nuclear weapons themselves. We have been pursuing this trail from one dead end to another, ever since Hiroshima. Despite our repeated failure, despite the evidence of the dangerous and deteriorating effects of this search for a Solution, we are still in the grip of that illusion.

CHAPTER III

—◦○◦—

ATOMIC BLIND ALLEYS

FROM THE YEAR 1945, our search for a Single Solution to the threat of the Bomb has led us through a series of all-embracing policies, or final answers. Every time such an answer has failed, another one has risen to take its place, each heralded in turn by its proponents as being, at last, the long-sought Solution, somehow better than its discarded predecessors.

Yet the differences have been superficial. All of these policies have been variations on the theme of Single Solution, and all have dealt almost exclusively with the problem of nuclear weapons. In our emotional fixation on these cure-alls, we have discounted other and less grandiose programs that might have a bearing on the threat of atomic war. Foreign aid to underdeveloped nations, international trade policies, international health programs—all such more prosaic efforts to increase, bit by bit, the common and constructive bonds of a world community have been regarded as being of secondary concern.

Let us look, then, at some of the policy assumptions about what we have, as a nation, regarded as the prime question. Each of these assumptions was once widely believed, and each has either become wholly discredited or at least gravely weakened by the force of new facts. In every instance, there has been a disturbing after-effect. The ghosts of these outmoded convictions about the Atomic Solution linger on, inhibiting the full and clear development of new and more realistic ideas.

Assumption No. 1: That, as to atomic weapons, "we had the secret"; that this gave us a monopoly on nuclear weapons for a substantial period of time so that the use or the threatened use of atomic weapons would assure the security of the United States and its friends; that we had the ultimate weapon so that the United States could police the world and insure a Pax Americana.

Underlying this premise was the comforting conviction—not shared by scientists—that this revolutionary discovery was not only a secret, but that the production of the first atomic bombs was based upon a scientific sensitivity and perception and industrial know-how unique to the United States of America, which the Soviet Union did not have.

In 1945 it was quite natural that most Americans should feel that development of a great atomic bomb was based upon a secret that could be written on a slip of paper and put in a safe. Indeed, this recalls an incident of Christmastime in 1946. The Manhattan District under General Leslie Groves was on the following day transferring all of the property, personnel, and weapons of the atomic establishment to a new civilian Atomic Energy Commission of which I was chairman. A newspaper photographer called the AEC Public Relations Department and asked: "Can you arrange for me to get a picture of General Groves handing the secret to Chairman Lilienthal?"

The monopoly assumption was jarred by a fact when in September 1949 the Soviet Union exploded its first nuclear device. Even then, in the very highest and presumably most knowledgeable United States circles, the first reaction was one of disbelief.

If our present policies are to make sense we must fully understand that not only is our nuclear monopoly gone, but with it the once widely used tranquilizer that there is *any* technical achievement an advanced industrial country, and notably the Soviet Union, is incapable of attaining. We should be realists enough to look at a world in which there is no such thing as a technical monopoly except for a brief period of time, among even the lesser industrial nations of the world.

Yet not long ago Admiral Rickover, a noted Naval engineer, a man to whom all of America is indebted, made a speech, in which, talking with justifiable pride of the nuclear-powered Polaris submarine he pioneered, he described this underseas weapon as a monopoly of the United States. This, he said, gave him a great sense of assurance. He then added that the secret by which the United States had produced so remarkable a military weapon as this submarine is ranked in importance with the development of the atomic bomb in 1945, and he went on to say that he hoped that this secret could be kept better than the atomic bomb secret of 1945.

That Admiral Rickover, who has on so many occasions described the educational strength of the Soviet Union in engineering and technology, should in 1962 still be talking about a technical monopoly—this time of a submarine—gives me pause.

I had assumed that this idea had become erased in the public mind. I had assumed that the Russian achievements in the field of rockets, far more complex than the development of an atomic submarine, had dispelled this notion.

Assumption No. 2: That nuclear weapons are substantially all we need for our military security; like "modern man," so-called conventional pre-Hiroshima arms are "obsolete." Infantry, a balanced army with a substantial reserve, a strong navy with a submarine fleet, a strengthened air force, fighter planes, tanks, paratroopers: under the atomic bomb mystique these were said to be virtually museum pieces, relics of the days before the "ultimate" weapon, the A-bomb. When my duties as a public servant put me in the midst of military matters, I heard much of this now-discredited doctrine.

This all-embracing nuclear bomb illusion, dressed up variously as "massive retaliation" or a "quantum jump" in weapons, persisted long after our own nuclear monopoly ended, and it still persists in other guises.

It was not, I should add, embraced by the men in the military establishment whom I happened to know best, such men as the brilliant General Lauris Norstad. And as everyone knows, it was repudiated by General Maxwell Taylor; indeed, so completely did he disagree with what he called the Great Fallacy that he found no alternative but to retire from active service in 1959. His reasons for disagreement he set out in his book; *An Uncertain Trumpet*.* General Taylor, who became Military Advisor to President Kennedy and more recently Chairman of the Joint Chiefs of Staff, has the satisfaction of knowing that his dignified protest helped to gain acceptance for the concept of a balanced military establishment, in which nuclear weapons and nuclear strategy take their place but are not our almost exclusive military reliance.

In considering whether it is futile and quixotic for anyone now to challenge present concepts, it is relevant to recall how deeply ingrained the all-powerful one-shot solution still was in 1949, at the time of the discussions on the crash program to develop the thermonuclear or H-bomb. It is also relevant in judging how much weight to give today to the opinions of those who continue to advocate that America's military security lies essentially in "bigger and better" nuclear weapons.

In 1949, while I was still Chairman of the AEC, what were described as "obsolete" and unneeded and

* Harper and Bros., New York, 1960.

31

expensive non-nuclear military forces were cut to the bone; indeed a good part of the bone was cut as well.

The Chairman of the Joint Chiefs at that time was the imperturbable, soft-voiced hero of World War II, General Omar Bradley. As we talked about my own responsibility in relation to his, he shocked me by a statement which he later made in almost the same terms in a public address. He said that we had reduced our military forces so severely in reliance on atomic weapons that we actually had no effective reserves. This was the condition when we were forced into the war in Korea.

How many American lives were needlessly lost in the Korean conflict because we were disarmed, except for atomic weapons which for military, political, and moral reasons were not used in that war, no one can estimate. The tragedy of a philosophy of giving the Atom a place of complete dominance was a poignant one. But we did not recognize this fallacy, despite the cruel lessons of Korea, until several years had passed.

For a time we were beguiled with a first cousin to the illusion that all we needed were A-bombs: the premise, passionately espoused, that H-bombs would give us the security A-bombs had failed to provide. The subsequent erosion of this assumption is relevant to my theme of the dangerous aberrations that flow from a preoccupation with nuclear weapons.

When the air-filters told us in September 1949 that in a short time the Russians would have atomic bombs, there were those who advocated, with passion and effectiveness, that our counter to the Russian A-bomb should be a crash program for this far bigger bomb, a super-bomb later called, of course, a hydrogen or thermonuclear bomb. Such weapons turned out later to have militarily useful qualities other than greater size, but it was greater potential size that won the case for the H-bomb in the hectic secret debate of early 1950.

There were those in the atomic energy activities of the Government then, in late 1949 and early 1950, among the best informed of men, who took the position that no such proposal should be railroaded through in panic over the news of the Russians' A-bomb success; that to start a new series of weapons of such fantastic destructiveness without sober reflection on where it might lead was reckless; there were indeed those who felt the consequences were so grave that the whole issue should be made a matter of public discussion in this country, and with the Russians.

At that time there might have been an opportunity to try something bold and imaginative entirely outside the weapons field, to improve the prospects of peace, but our obsession with bigger bombs as a cure-all excluded any serious consideration of such a possibility. Who can say today with assurance that such an imaginative move might not have changed the grim course of subsequent history?

There were those in 1950—I was one of them—who

argued that as a minimum condition to committing ourselves to a crash program for a super-bomb there should be a concurrent expansion and diversification of our non-nuclear forces. We wanted careful thought given to the question whether the H-bomb could do what the A-bomb could not do for national security. Some of us wanted to know whether the projected super-bomb had military value or only, as one general put it "psychological value." We wanted to know how such a weapon could be delivered to a target. Astute colleagues of mine asserted that unless we also had long-range or intercontinental missiles the military value of a super-bomb was doubtful, compared with existing A-bombs. Did it make sense to develop a super-bomb without a simultaneous all-out effort to insure that such a weapon could be effectively used for military purposes?

Such questions were summarily brushed aside by most of the one-track proponents of the super-bomb. Any weapon the Soviets might be able to produce we must have, too. In all sincerity this simple doctrine was offered and accepted as a complete answer to all our questions about the crash H-bomb program. Such a simple formula, I dare say, would satisfy no one today.

As a gesture of conciliation to the views that I had then presented, written assurance was given that a reassessment of our whole military position would be made, with a view to strengthening our conventional forces. Accordingly, I did not press our reservations further. With an appraisal of our posture on conventional arms explicitly attached as a condition, the H-bomb crash program was launched. I should add that the strengthening of conventional arms was promptly put on the shelf, only to be made effective years later, when disenchantment with the effectiveness of the one-shot solution of the H-bomb had set in.

Thus our policy was fixed: to put vast energies into the development of this super-weapon, not only to the almost disastrous neglect of the less dramatic conventional branches of warfare, but to the neglect of the best and perhaps the only way by which the super-bomb itself could be made fully effective, intercontinental ballistic missiles.

This overvaluation of the super-bomb as a cure-all, which dominated our policy in 1950 and for so many years thereafter, may have been responsible in part for the state of underemphasis we found in our rocketry program when Sputnik woke us up.

Assumption No. 3: That atomic bombs are so destructive that "modern man is obsolete"; that the fearful power of the A-bomb makes world government the only course open to man.

On a visit to Los Alamos as early as 1946 I was briefed on the possibility, known for some years by scientists, that some form of super-bomb a thousand or more times as destructive as the Hiroshima A-bomb might be feasible. The code name was revealing: Alarm Clock. A distinguished staff member explained this nickname to me: such a weapon, if it could be made, would so frighten the world as to awaken men to the absolute necessity for world government, at once. We still hear this virtue of Big Bombs from the innocents among present-day weaponeers and civilian "strategists."

This obsession about the power of fear to reconstitute man's institutions, to rob him of his passions and his hates, to relocate his loyalties, is another casualty of the realities. The facts are that fear of destruction, fear of death, fear of catastrophe, play a role in man's affairs, as they always have; but fear is not the foundation upon which it is possible overnight, or in a decade, or even in a generation to design a new structure of human affairs, much less to erect one and make it function.

The failure of the assumption that we could create effective world government through fear of the Bomb is a bitter illustration of the price of the Single Solution myth.

If there is one and only one Solution, and if this Solution fails, then there is no alternative but despair. It is not surprising, therefore, that some of those who had pressed most stridently the theme of world-government-or-else should later reappear as the spokesmen for a policy of hopelessness, accepting the inevitability of disaster.

Assumption No. 4: An Underground America. This is the most flamboyant and irresponsible of all the assumptions or premises for dealing with the nuclear threat by dealing exclusively with nuclear weapons: the building of an underground country as "passive defense" against nuclear war.

"I believe," wrote Dr. Edward Teller in 1960, "that an extensive shelter program would save the great majority of the people of the United States, even in the case of a most ferocious attack"—at a cost of 80 billion dollars. This and similar recommendations and proffers of life, from such august sources as Dr. Teller, set off a crusade. The President, Congressmen, Mayors, Governors, University Trustees, and individuals went all out for a hole-in-the-ground program. Many scientists, speaking as men with common sense and human values, and who as scientists knew how technically futile this idea is on such a scale, warned against it to no avail, at the time. Yet less than a year after the onset of this nation-wide campaign it was difficult to find any but the remnants of the back-to-your-caves movement.

Assumption No. 5: "Atoms for Peace." President Eisenhower's Atoms for Peace Program launched before the United Nations is another casualty, still alive but in a wheelchair. As a result of his moving espousal of this step toward an end of nuclear despair, an international atomic agency was set up and is operating, manned by exceptionally qualified people. But the prospects that this program can do much about ending the threat of nuclear war by reducing nuclear stockpiles or gain experience in "inspection" techniques to guard the peace seem at the moment dim.

I could list other assumptions and fads that in a brief time have gone by the boards, casualties of the facts or of more realistic thinking. For example the doctrine, in a verbally impressive book by Professor Henry Kissinger, of "limited" nuclear war. The life of this vogue was, however, unusually short. Dr. Kissinger lost little time in giving it decent burial—in another book.

My purpose in reviewing these outmoded convictions of past years has been to demonstrate that we already have, however haltingly and however unwillingly, abandoned certain basic assumptions or obsessions about nuclear weapons and the way out of the horrors they hold.

All these positions, I think, had essentially the same foundation, a preoccupation with atomic weapons themselves as the key to world peace, to world government, to the containment of Communism, or to the maintenance, if not of peace or peace of mind, of a kind of world stability, or at least survival.

Let us take a look at our *present* policies. They are also founded on that same major premise: that the primary answer to the dangers of nuclear warfare are to be found almost exclusively within the area of nuclear weapons.

The *first* of these current premises is this: We must

maintain a powerful nuclear force; this should be combined with a strengthening of overall conventional military forces, but with the predominant emphasis upon nuclear weapons. We should include weapons in large numbers and of very great power (although here the H-bomb euphoria of 1950 about the virtues of increasing the destructive power of individual weapons seems to be declining). This doctrine now emphasizes delivery systems capable of putting these weapons on targets, and these delivery systems must be as nearly invulnerable to enemy attack as possible.

A nuclear shield does not by any manner of means provide a complete answer for security or peace, but it is the only *military* alternative now open to us.

Our present thinking lays great stress on the idea of mutual deterrent; that is, that peace can be kept by nuclear weapons where each of the antagonists is strong enough to destroy the other. To put it more explicitly, the argument is that nuclear weapons are a step toward peace if the United States and the Soviet Union are both so strongly armed that it is too hazardous to their objectives for either side to make use of them. Under this doctrine neither antagonist can allow the other to outdistance him in nuclear weapons; otherwise the deterrent or stalemate may not be effective.

This is supposed to be a kind of atomic balance of power. But the more nuclear weapons and missiles to carry them we have, the more the Soviets drive themselves to outdo us; the more nuclear striking power the

Soviets acquire to put themselves "ahead" of us, the more effort we then are compelled to exert to outdo them, or to widen the gap, as the journalistic phrase has it. And so on and on. The West and the Soviets are caught in a seesaw. The concept of "balance of power," or the concept of a parity of power as a means of stability, does not have its classic meaning when weapons of such magnitude are in the hands of antagonists. For even the weaker of two nuclear antagonists, as things stand today, can virtually destroy the other, and be destroyed in the process. The balance is one not of power in any meaningful sense of the term.

Nevertheless I myself see no present alternative to maintaining our nuclear shield. The paradox of building up nuclear arms so great as to be unusable as an instrument for the waging of war is basic in the West, and it would appear to be equally firmly held by the Soviet Union.

Here again the assumption is that we avoid nuclear war by what we do with nuclear weapons.

The *second basic premise* upon which we now erect our hopes for peace moves in what would appear to be the opposite direction, though it is curiously parallel to the first premise. It, too, is preoccupied with and centered upon nuclear weapons.

The best hope, so this premise states, of preventing world-wide nuclear war is by putting an end to the arms competition through a negotiated program of *disarmament* with the USSR. The current proposals by both the United States and the Soviet Union have been couched in language of a program of general and total disarmament, but the crucial phase deals with nuclear weapons.

We are told on high authority that disarmament is "the most seriously pressed proposal for the achievement of peace"; our President has admonished the world that "The weapons of war must be abolished before they abolish us."

Both our present policy and the largely discredited and abandoned policies of past years are erected on the same foundation, the passionate belief that there is and must be a Single Solution to the threat of atomic war, and that this Solution may be found in the area of atomic weapons.

It is not difficult to point to the dead or dying assumptions of the past and say that these have failed. Obviously they have.

We must now examine our *present* policy and see whether it, too, may be likely to suffer the same fate—and why.

41

CHAPTER IV

———●○●———

THE MYTHOLOGY OF NUCLEAR

DISARMAMENT

E V E R Y O N E   R E C O G N I Z E S what a terrible disaster the use of nuclear weapons on a large scale can bring to the world. Here there are no important differences of opinion. The area of difference lies in the answers to the question: What can be done about this threat of disaster, and how?

There are at least three different points of view among us:

First: Get rid of the weapons; disarmament by negotiation with the Soviet Union, pressed as the highest priority among men. Either disarm or perish.

Second: Give the negotiation of a disarmament agreement top priority, even while recognizing that the prospects of complete agreement in the near future are far from bright. But keep at the negotiations. Meanwhile seek also other ways by which tensions and animosities between nations, and especially the atomic powers, can be reduced and relieved so as to make the top priority, a negotiated disarmament (or arms control, if one prefers the expression), more likely of achievement.

This is a far from an unreasonable view; it is held

by many for whom I have great respect. In my opinion, however, this course does not give proper weight to the dangers to peace and to ultimate disarmament that lie in the *very process of seeking to negotiate disarmament treaties* in the present state of acute animosity and fear that exists between the powers, including China. Moreover, this course does not adequately recognize that such a preoccupation with disarmament distracts and dilutes our attention, our faith, our energies and our political, physical, and spiritual resources from far more hopeful and realistic plural roads towards peace, outside the area of arms and disarmament.

In a subsequent chapter I shall invite the reader to consider a third course that represents my own conviction, reached after more than a decade of careful thought, but let us now examine disarmament as it is proposed in the two points of view just presented.

The road to eliminating nuclear war is said to be disarmament. I say "said to be" because this is the official verbal position of the great powers, and it is the great tranquilizer for the anxious lay citizen on our side and perhaps both sides of the Iron Curtain.

The formal position of both the United States and the USSR places serious steps in disarmament highest on officially stated priorities, so we must consider it a major premise although the acts of rearmament of both governments tend the other way.

For several years the Russians and ourselves (as

chief parties) have been at the conference table at Geneva on what is described as a first step in disarmament, that is, an attempt to agree not to test nuclear weapons. It is not surprising that these disarmament efforts have not at this writing produced agreement, although it is possible that some form of agreement on testing, or a de facto suspension, may be within reach.

Whatever action may or may not be taken on the test-ban question, it seems all too clear to me that the primary object of these conferences, the reduction and ultimately the abolition of nuclear arms, is doomed to failure. The conditions that would make possible any kind of agreement simply do not exist.

I will further assert that the very process of negotiating at this time actually produces an effect opposite to the purpose of the conferences, that is, a lessening of the tensions between the two great power blocs.

Let me try to support these assertions. First, that the primary object of the conferences at Geneva is at this time impossible of achievement.

The discussions about disarmament have assumed two antagonists. A commitment on the part of the Soviet Union for disarmament is presumed, under this doctrine, to encompass wholly one side of the balance of power, and the same is to be said of the West. But the fluidity of the world is such that the Soviet Union may not even now be able to speak for the countries that are or may be major threats to peace. It is almost certain today that the Soviet Union would be unable to commit China to disarmament. With the West and the Soviet disarmed the Chinese could make a mockery of the very objective of disarmament: peace in the world.

Even a serious prospect that both the great powers *might* disarm could be disturbing to peace-loving peoples in Asia, under the shadow of China.

On the other side (but to a lesser degree) it is far from clear that the United Kingdom and the United States could now speak for the Republic of France on a disarmament program, perhaps even on a test ban.

Disarmament, as a principal reliance for peace, has this inherent defect, that unless it is well-nigh universal it increases the power for mischief of those who are unwilling to disarm, or who change sides.

In our own time we have seen almost overnight shifts in who is enemy and who is friend. On one day the strongest military nation in Europe, the German Reich, was on the friendliest terms with Russia, and on the following day, waging war with her.

Who would have thought, in the year 1946, say, that within a short span of years we would not only be permitting the Japanese and Germans to rearm, but be very anxious lest they not be rearming on a large enough scale? Our bitter and implacable enemies of the Forties now have become among our more powerful allies; and of course some of our allies of that time, Russia and mainland China, are allies no longer.

In 1951 I talked in India with Prime Minister Nehru, and I recorded and published these conversations at some length.

What I hoped he could give me, I said to Mr. Nehru, would be perspective that would enable me and other Americans better to understand Asia and India. I supposed that no one in the world was better equipped to respond to such a request for perspective.

Late at night, after his long day's work, or under the trees in the garden of the official residence, Mr. Nehru gave me at length his picture of the historic ties that bound China and India together. "In the far-off times," he said, before the Europeans came to Asia, "India and China were close together . . . tied . . . by the bonds of trade and religion and culture. . . . An upsurge of independence, of nationalism, has swept China, Burma, Indochina and elsewhere. Out of this long, long common experience the bonds that once held China and India together again emerge more clearly than for hundreds of years. Not because of common belief in Communism—not at all; the ties I speak of go back hundreds of years. . . ."

This was not, I think, wishful thinking on Mr. Nehru's part. Yet, as we know, these ties of time immemorial did not prevent the outbreak of armed hostilities in 1962, only a decade later. Few things better illustrate the tidal waves of change in the present-day world in which it would seem that nothing is unchanging, nothing is inevitable except change itself.

If the pieces on the armament chess board are moving with such unpredictable rapidity, is this not a dangerous time to engage in serious negotiations with the Soviet Union about complete and total disarmament; is this a time when anything but continued futility, frustration, and increased hostility can come out of such negotiations?

The answer can only be that we are *not* engaging in serious negotiations with the Soviet Union. All other considerations aside, the absence of Red China from these discussions makes them a futile exercise. The Russian leaders are not fools, nor are our own. Do we expect the Russians to agree to any significant reduction in their military strength through a process that binds them and us but not the aggressive Chinese? Would *we,* on our side, wish to be similarly committed?

The conclusion is obvious—and most obvious, one can be sure, to the very leaders in the West who find themselves forced for the vague justification of "world propaganda" to speak of the disarmament conferences as if they represented a real hope instead of a patent illusion, what a leading Senator calls mumbo-jumbo.

My second assertion is that the negotiations at Geneva, although conducted by able and patient men, have not improved the prospects for avoiding nuclear disaster but have instead subtracted from the prospects of peace.

Take one instance only. Ironically, this instance arises out of the sole issue of principle on which the

USA and the USSR have reached verbal agreement.

In September 1961 Ambassadors McCloy and Zorin agreed for their governments, and I quote a portion of the central clause, that "all measures of general and complete disarmament should be balanced so that at no stage of the implementation of the treaty could any state or group of states gain military advantage" as a consequence of disarmament measures.

How can these bitter antagonists discuss a "balance" of military force as between them, so that the discussion will make any sense at all, without disclosing to the other the state of their arms at the time of the balancing process? And information in sufficiently revealing detail to mean anything inevitably discloses to knowledgeable men their war plans and military policies. War policies and plans are a nation's most sensitive area, making the controversial "on-site" inspection of underground tests seem innocuous indeed by comparison. And how can discussion of "balance" make any sense unless the disclosures and representations of the two parties of their present arms are subjected to verification by the other side? The incentive for lying, or saber-rattling to impress the other side, would be brought to a new high point if such a discussion got very far. What a bagful of furies the specific discussion of such propositions might unleash! What acute anxieties it would stir! How much nearer this could bring us to the point of no return!

There are more than a few instances growing out

of the negotiations of disarmament and of the test ban that have led to and will continue to lead to provocative and dangerous charges of bad faith on both sides. These are directed not just against the negotiators, but they inevitably challenge the honor and intentions of the heads of state and their chief civilian and military officers. Repeatedly calling into question the honesty and intentions of a great power, in the ugly temper of the present, inflicts wounds that fester. When the dispute in negotiation concerns fishery rights that is one thing. But where the questions are those of life and death that are involved in disarmament discussions, that is quite another matter, for while these talks go on the very subjects of discussion—their nuclear missiles, and ours—are pointed toward each other night and day. Under these conditions an accusation that impugns an antagonist's basic intentions *about those very weapons* increases the risk that the trigger will be pulled by design or in panic, since such as accusation may well be construed as the signal for attack, forcing what a military man might readily justify as "anticipatory retaliation."

Thus the very discussions intended by both sides to diminish distrust and promote better relations can produce grave, acute, and even explosive mutual crises of confidence. These are the dangers of the Geneva negotiations, grave dangers indeed, and risks not worth running in view of the futility of achieving any offsetting benefits. For those millions throughout the world who believe that these conferences are being undertaken seriously by the major powers, they are an escape from reality in this tough and changing world. The awakening will come, and it will be a bitter one, as damaging and disheartening to the hopes of mankind as have been similar frustrations of this cold-war period.

The Russians have made it evident that Geneva means nothing more to them than a propaganda springboard. From time to time, as in the past, Chairman Khrushchev will make some dramatic disarmament move, couched in conciliatory terms. This will, if the past is any measure, encourage a belief among many people that disarmament is in truth a real hope. As a consequence there will once more be a diminution of vigor and faith and public interest in those more prosaic measures for peace that lie outside the area of weapons. The Russians have done this more than once before, Chairman Khrushchev coming to the United States at one time for that purpose. It is bound to happen again in a somewhat different form, perhaps at Geneva and possibly soon.

Such proffers stir hopes in an anxious world, and then nothing comes of them except disappointment and despair, until the next occasion when the Soviet leaders find it opportune to raise an illusion of some kind of settlement that they do not, or *cannot*, really mean.

We have been through just such periods of unreality and wishful thinking in recent years—the Spirit of

Geneva, the Spirit of Camp David, the illusions of the summit meeting formula for peace. In the spring of 1960 we had just been through two years of this fantasy; what I wrote then expresses as well as I can today the risks of unrealism. In an article in the *New York Times* for May 15, 1960, I said: "The sure road to war is to live in fantasy, in a world that does not exist. . . . It is through such a dream world that the west has been passing. During this incredible period, however, the hard-bitten, realistic and aggressive Communists were softening up our American resolution—their prime target.

"They flooded us with horror stories of 'mutual suicide' by atomic warfare and alluring but empty offers of 'peaceful coexistence,' total disarmament and an end to nuclear weapons. . . .

"There is a wealth of impressive evidence that the American people can face hard, cruel and disappointing facts, and can act with vigor, toughness, tenacity and firmness. . . .

"It was American firmness and readiness to face up to facts, that helped get the Red Army out of Iran, that rebuilt our armed forces and thereby kept the Chinese out of South Korea, that saved Greece and Turkey, that helped produce a peace treaty for Austria, that saved Berlin by an amazing airlift. On almost any of these acts of resolution the Soviet might have gone to war. They didn't."

51

If I were writing this today I would not change it except to add the Cuban crisis to the list.

Resuming: "A peace that is no peace, a thaw that is no warming up . . . —this is not the road to peace. On the contrary, it is the road to disaster."

And then this final paragraph of that article: "There is as yet no evidence that facing up to reality in dealing with the Soviet adds to the risks that already exist. My own opinion is that the greatest risk of all would be to continue to nurse the illusion that international tension is relaxed because we ourselves have been relaxing."

The average man and the conscientious realistic public servant may fully realize that the Geneva negotiations at this time are futile. Yet the feeling is widespread, I would judge, among very well motivated people that such negotiations are the only hope; or that they must be continued however slender the prospects, since we cannot allow the Russians to say that we do not want disarmament and that, therefore, we do not want peace.

I find that there are not a few thoughtful people who say, to justify futile and ill-timed negotiations, "While you are talking you're not shooting."

I wonder. I recall that the Japanese emissaries were still talking to Secretary Hull while their bombardiers were blasting our fleet at Pearl Harbor.

Or take a recent case. On October 30, 1962, the Indian Ambassador to the United States issued a statement to his countrymen here concerning China's attack on India. "From the very beginning of this [border] dispute we had never stinted any effort to arrive at a peaceful solution through negotiation. . . . *While talking of negotiations* China has prepared for aggression and has now launched a totally unprovoked massive armed invasion against us."

Talking is not always synonymous with not shooting. Talking around a conference table *unless* the parties have something specific to say, something that is feasible and that will be supported by their people back home, has little to commend it.

There is a deeper reason why we must consider the current negotiations for disarmament with the utmost seriousness, and question them if we feel, as I do, that they should be challenged. For whether the negotiators believe there will be affirmative results of their efforts or not, they are necessarily prisoners of a commitment, an emotional commitment, to the premise which I regard as a myth: that hope for eliminating war lies chiefly or solely in eliminating weapons of war.

I know of nothing in modern experience and history that supports the thesis that disarmament in itself brings peace. Indeed I would be prepared to defend the proposition that our almost total disarmament after World War II increased the tensions in the world and gave the Soviet Union the opportunity to create underlying causes of war with which we now are saddled for an indefinite period.

I deny that the nature of man makes it sensible to assume that there will be conflicts that can always be rationally resolved, and that these conflicts will not at times eventuate in violence. With equal conviction I contradict those able, learned men who assert that it is "inevitable" that a continuance of the so-called arms race *must* lead to nuclear war. In a changing world nothing is inevitable—except further change.

More affirmatively, I ask you to consider whether the prospects for changes that will make nuclear armaments less relevant, that will minimize the risk that they will be used, or any arms used, is not far greater if we look for and encourage those heartening developments among peoples and nations which do not have nuclear arms as their central theme. The slow growth of community among men—here is the true disarmament.

When I say true disarmament, I suggest that simply dismantling missiles as a part of a negotiated disarmament treaty may or may not be true disarmament. It is not nuclear weapons that are at the center of our problems. It is man. Nuclear weapons in Canada are no threat to us; the same weapons at the same distance, in Cuba, are a threat, and those weapons had to be removed. The difference is not in the presence of weapons but the purposes of the men behind them—their motives, their grievances, the desperation of their leaders because of internal pressures, the poverty of racial hysteria, or the grievances of their people—in short, the whole bundle of human emotional combustibles which cause war.

I have a deep confidence that in time the world will find ways of composing most differences and conflicts, but we shall always have to contend with conflicts and competition and struggle and the impulse to use force. They are built into the nature of man himself, but in the nature of man are also God-like qualities of reason, compassion, compromise, and love, not only for his own family but for the family of man.

Surely our leaders recognize full well that the disarmament conference is futile. They presumably feel that we are trapped in it for propaganda reasons and cannot gracefully withdraw without something better to offer world opinion.

But what disturbs me most about Geneva is that it feeds and perpetuates the myth of Single Solution. It is merely the latest manifestation of the emotional fix we have been in since Hiroshima. When Geneva has finally faded away we will, I am afraid, still find ourselves in this unreal Atomic world: there will be some other panacea, some other sweeping plan or program which will solve everything—on paper. And we will be in for another bout of wishful thinking, while the bombs continue to multiply and the tensions continue to grow.

The crime of this mythology is not only that it is unrealistic and dangerous but that it involves an incalculable waste of human hopes and diversion of energies and imagination. The constructive jobs that *can be done* in this fluid and changing world are manifold and challenging. For the most part they have nothing directly to do with nuclear weapons or the threat posed by these weapons, and yet, as I will attempt to describe in a later chapter, it is just these manageable jobs in areas quite removed from weapons that constitute our true hope, that hold out not the abstract guarantees of blueprinted Solutions but understandable human possibilities of peace.

Our preoccupation with Solutions—and Geneva happens to be only the current one—keeps us from wholeheartedly pursuing what I believe to be the many roads and paths to a real disarmament, the diverse ways and means of strengthening the sense of community in the world, a world in which weapons would become less and less relevant.

We must deal with the world as it is, we must begin from where we are and move toward the noble goals of peace to which we all aspire. Competition, passion, hate, love, imagination—all the factors that make up everyday living—are among the essential components of the most sensitive human problem man has ever sought to deal with—living in peace among his fellow men on this earth. This is a matter too great, too complex, too burdened with the history and yearnings of mankind to be capable of solution by experts sitting at a conference table.

At the close of the Second World War in complete

good faith we occupied ourselves with programs for the nuclear disarmament of the victorious alliance, the United States, the United Kingdom, France, and the USSR. How adversely this preoccupation with weapons, continued since that time, eroded the relations between the members of that alliance no man can yet assess. But we can say that the disarmament movement after the First World War *did* produce disastrous results. One of the brilliant apostles of disarmament after World War I was the man who is now America's most respected political analyst, Mr. Walter Lippmann. In a book written in 1943* he explained why he had been wrong in crusading for disarmament. I ask you to ponder Mr. Lippmann's words and decide for yourselves whether or not they are relevant to the problem we have faced ever since the end of World War II.

"In the interval between the two great wars the United States sought to promote peace by denouncing war, even by 'outlawing it,' and by disarming itself, Great Britain and France . . . the disinterested and idealistic theory of disarmament was that if everyone had less capacity to wage war, there would be a smaller likelihood of war. Big warships meant big wars. Smaller warships meant smaller wars. No warships might eventually mean no wars. . . . On the theory that disarmament could promote peace, laborious negotiations and elaborate diplomacy and splendid international con-

* *U.S. Foreign Policy*, Little Brown & Co., Boston, 1943.

ferences were promoted in Washington, Geneva, and London. . . . It soon transpired that though the premise of these conferences was that smaller armaments would banish war, the working premise of all the governments was that each of the former allies was now the rival, and therefore the potential enemy, of all the others. The disarmament movement was, as the event has shown, tragically successful in disarming the nations that believed in disarmament. The net effect was to dissolve the alliance among the victors of the First World War, and to reduce them to almost disastrous impotence. . . ."

I have said that our chief hope for peace is not in an attack on weapons but in other areas of life. To an elaboration of this thesis I shall return in a later chapter. Meanwhile I want to explore further some other aspects of our preoccupation with the Atom.

CHAPTER V

———○———

WHAT THE ATOM IS DOING TO
SCIENCE AND SCIENTISTS

W E K N O W what science has done to the Atom,
but what is the Atom doing to science and scientists?

We know that in our own time scientists have un-
covered, layer by layer, the fundamental nature and
composition of matter. This burst of creative genius
is the distinctive achievement of the human imagination and spirit of this century. As a consequence we
all share a sense of living in an heroic time. For this
achievement our time will be remembered, as today
we look back upon an explosion of special genius in
the arts, poetry, and literature in the days of Leonardo,
of Michelangelo, of Shakespeare. The respect and even
adulation for science by laymen has stimulated interest
in the whole of education. As a result there is greater
reverence for learning, a wider recognition of the value
of the imaginative power of man's mind.

The dazzling achievements of the atomic physicists
have led the way either directly or by example to important discoveries in virtually every other area of
science; it has become a commonplace to say that
science and scientists are playing an increasingly decisive role in our lives. But the new authority and

prestige of science and scientists have been accompanied by the vulnerabilities and anxieties of power. Great changes have taken place in the role of the scientist, and severe tensions are evident today within the scientific community.

Before attempting an evaluation of what is happening to science and scientists, I would like to note what many people seem to have forgotten, that science is not an abstract, disembodied force; it is the work of men, of individuals. It is, in its finest form, an expression of man's determination to understand the natural world. In this the scientist is driven by much the same force that torments and fulfills the artist and the poet. His work springs from the highest, purest, and most creative impulses in man.

Any one man's capacity to evaluate what the Atom has done and is doing to science and scientists is certainly limited, but the limitation does not arise solely out of the fact that, as in my case, he is a layman. The tapestry of science has become so intricate that there are few, if any, scientists who are not "laymen" outside the small area of their specialty. Being a layman, therefore, is not a fatal handicap in the reassessment of what is happening to science and scientists. Indeed, in some ways it may be an advantage, for to a degree the future course of science depends on an understanding not of complex technical content but of science's basic purposes as an expression of a deep human need to know.

So in this chapter one layman, who has been responsible for the work of scientists and technical men over a long period, will record some observations and conclusions about science and scientists two decades after the achievement of the controlled release of nuclear energy. It is especially timely to make such a reassessment now, for these past twenty years have seen a revitalization of science that cannot be matched in the whole history of human creativity.

The evidence increases that we are in the midst of a crisis in the scientific community, and of a period of bewilderment, disagreement, and anxiety about the role of science. These deep doubts and misgivings, first felt among the scientists themselves, have now spread widely. This increasing crisis of confidence in science and scientists, now approaching the momentum of an avalanche, may be difficult to retard once the stage of sliding has begun. This incipient avalanche, I would judge, has its origin not in any lack of respect or recognition for science in its classic role, as that aspect of human genius by which we gain knowledge of the natural world. The crisis of doubts about science has its roots in concern that science and scientists have more and more been seeking to apply methods applicable to the physical world to areas of the world of men that are beyond the reach of their methods: human goals and purposes, human priorities, human motivations.

The questionings and doubts about science seem to me to arise as a consequence of scientists' involvement and leadership in at least three kinds of nonscientific areas of human affairs:

(1) Scientists and technical men have played a leading part in fathering and promoting the idea that there is some Single Solution to the threat of nuclear war. Increasing (though belated) recognition of the basic defect of this approach has injured public confidence in scientists, and hence in science; it has shaken scientists' confidence in themselves.

(2) Scientists have—unwittingly, perhaps, at first—been in part responsible for diluting the spirit of independent inquiry that is the very core of science, by becoming uncritical advocates and even lobbyists for various huge "programmatic" technical enterprises, of which atomic energy and the space program are but two instances.

(3) The scientific "boom" under government sponsorship that followed the splitting of the Atom has resulted in a rapid and disturbing alteration in the nature and functioning of our colleges and universities. Some of our major universities are becoming scientific dukedoms rather than institutions of higher learning. The scientists may still bear the honored scholarly title of professor, but in actuality they are the devisers, promoters, and administrators of projects being carried out under contracts or grants—and have little or nothing to do with teaching or basic research.

SCIENCE AND THE SCIENTISTS

I

How scientists came to be so deeply committed to finding a way of ending the terrible dangers of atomic armaments is not difficult to see. Theirs was the work which led to the bombing of Hiroshima. A Single Solution to the complex problems of the release of the Atom's energy had been found by scientists; what more logical than that those same scientists should also find a Single Solution to its control?

It is well to recall the temper of those early days of the Atom. No predictions seemed too fantastic, whether of the doom of civilization through nuclear holocaust or of a world beneficently transformed through the peaceful use of this great new source of energy. Men were convinced that they were living in a world in which only the Atom counted, and man was almost incidental.

The Atom became all-important, and so therefore did the men who had called it into being, the atomic scientists. These men, whose skills lay in the handling of abstract concepts and inanimate physical materials, were suddenly catapulted into the very center of human affairs. Military men, politicians, business leaders, teachers—all categories of men who dealt with the more ornery and unpredictable affairs of human beings—were dwarfed by comparison. The scientist seemed to take on some of the attributes of his world-shaking creation; there was, in the public mind, something unearthly, something superhuman, something uncanny about him.

The widely held assumption among laymen was that the scientist was infallible *within* his field; that in the field of science there existed certain truths which, once discovered, were immutable and beyond dispute. Laymen were conditioned to believe that a scientist did not make errors, nor did he come up with what was only partly true; he quite simply learned Truths. The element of human judgment and fallibility was thought to be absent from science.

The scientist's mastery of nature, as so dramatically evidenced by the Atom, was expected therefore to lead to the conquest of hunger, of poverty, and of the greatest of human ills: war. As "master of the Atom," the scientist had transformed the world. His views on all subjects were sought by newspapermen, by Congressional committees, by organizations of all kinds; he was asked in effect to transfer his scientific mastery to the analysis of the very different questions of human affairs: peace, world government, social organization, population control, military strategy, and so forth. And his authority in these nonscientific areas was, at least at first, not strongly questioned.

Now, of course, most mature and responsible scientists climbed very quickly off the pedestal on which they had been so abruptly elevated. Dr. Eugene P. Wigner is only one of the many men of science who know the great functions but also the limitations of scientists in the broad area of public affairs. Recently he asked "why scientists so consistently overestimate the realizability of what appears to them the rational solution." "It is, in my opinion," he continued, "because they are not sufficiently aware of the phenomenon of the conflict of desires. If the rulers of the USSR want to extend their power over Hungary and the U.S. wants it otherwise, a rational solution can be found just as little as when two men want to marry the same girl."

As the man on the street knows, the "conflict of desires" is what makes life interesting but often irrational and sometimes bloody. Resolving the "conflict of desires" is the basic task of the ordinary layman in his daily life, as it is that of the man of affairs, in government, and in business—and as it is in the furious rivalries and defense of vested interests in the academic community, too, for that matter.

There were other men of science who tasted their new-found glory and found it very much to their liking—and still do. They sincerely believed that they had a special talent for solving global problems of human affairs on a "scientific basis." Even some of those who knew that human business is not science, who knew that they had no more claim to wisdom than the next fellow, decided quite reasonably to use their sudden public esteem for the most honorable of objects: the creation of a truly effective world organization to maintain the peace. They may have had some initial qualms about the validity of the attention given their articles and speeches; these were effectively overcome by the knowledge that they were fighting for the cause of peace and the security of the free world. Thus many scientists, for various and mixed reasons— dedication, nobility, personal vainglory—came into public prominence, and many have so remained, either in the open or as behind-the-scenes ghost-thinkers for political figures.

It seems to me that many scientists in the course of the last fifteen years have given reinforcement to the naïve point of view about the Atom and human affairs that has frustrated and confused our thinking. More than any other influential group, they have succeeded in espousing the doctrine of panacea: that in human affairs "*A Solution* can be found." Time and again they have discovered such Solutions, or lent the weight of their technical prestige to Solutions proposed by non-scientists.

This is a revival in different form of the old technocrat dogma: that all problems are basically technical, susceptible of precise analysis and correct and final solution. In this view, human emotions are hardly relevant, and in fact individual human behavior is an irritating distraction, for it introduces a vexing and nonscientific element of chance and unpredictability.

The most recent Solution, as we have seen, is disarmament (or "arms control"), and the classic pronouncement of the view of the primacy of this Solution has been given by Sir Charles Snow, fluent spokesman for the New Technocracy. In an address to the American Association for the Advancement of Science on December 27, 1960, Sir Charles said: "We are faced with an 'either-or,' and we haven't much time. Either we accept a restriction of nuclear armaments, [and he adds that such a course involves risks] . . . or . . . the nuclear arms race between the USA and the USSR not only continues but accelerates . . . within at the most ten years, some of these bombs are going off. . . . On the one side, therefore, we have a finite risk. On the other side we have a certainty of disaster. Between a risk and a certainty, a sane man does not hesitate. It is the plain duty of scientists to explain this 'either-or.' It is a duty which seems to me to come from the moral nature of the scientific activity itself."

With Sir Charles' concept of absolutes in human affairs—"either-or"—I profoundly disagree. It seems to me to epitomize how ill-adapted is the scientific method to deal with the contradictory, bewildering "conflicts of desires" that move and shake the world of men.

And yet we are witnessing the creation of a Scientific Establishment, a wide range of technical experts, "policy analysts," whose function is to guide us to a Solution to the threat of war (or tell us how to prevail in war if war should come). They are the new doctrinaires of the nuclear world, the new scholastics engaged in arguments about how many on-site inspections or game-theory hypotheses can be balanced, so to speak, on the head of a pin.

These are fluent and verbally clever men. The dreary spectacle of futility at Geneva should not blind us to the risk that some day we may find ourselves wedded to some of their methodology or doctrine, whether on disarmament or weapons, evolved in disregard of the complex underlying issues which are not technical at all. Laymen are too readily impressed by specialists whose concepts and even whose words they cannot comprehend. A scientist, reviewing a book by Dr. Herman Kahn, a high priest of the emerging cult of game-theory and operational analysis as a guide to human affairs, recently reminded his readers that "Department of Defense consultants back to the Delphic Oracle and before have consciously or unconsciously commanded respect by emphasizing the subtlety of their expertise and the dignity of their research organizations." That these dozens of "research organizations" are not communities of independent scholars but have as their principal clients and financial patrons agencies of our Government is not made apparent by their corporate or scholarly-sounding names: The RAND Corporation, The Hudson Institute, The Institute for Defense Analysis, and so on.

We must not at our peril exaggerate the usefulness of any narrow expertise, in the decision-making process in human affairs. We need to be alert to the danger of becoming the captives of this latter-day technocracy, this Atomic Solution Factory, which was originally erected on the tremendous prestige of the atomic scientists.

But a major re-evaluation is beginning. The failure of the laboratory approach to the vast human problems bound up in the Atom has been clear for some time now, and the reaction is setting in. The scientists themselves are becoming disturbed. Not long ago I was visited by a distinguished man of science who has been a leader in the scientist-dominated world-government-or-else movement. He confessed that he and some of his colleagues now have grave doubts about their almost sole preoccupation with disarmament and overnight world government. He agreed that in their passionate concentration on what is beyond the scope of practical achievement he and his scientific friends had neglected innumerable minor but tangible *possibilities* that do exist for helping to bind men together in common peaceful purpose the world over.

Well, I asked him, if your point of view has changed now, what are you going to do about it? Why don't you speak out, assert your leadership? This shook him. He had obviously been thinking about it himself. He said: "I can't do anything about it. Our scientific colleagues in other countries would not understand. No matter where an international peace conference attended by scientists begins," he added sadly, "it always veers to disarmament, or arms control, and nothing else seems to interest the conferees for long."

I have never myself attended a Pugwash or similar international conference, but I find my visitor's analysis revealing—and not without a certain pathos. Not only this man but many other members of the scientific community are having these grave second thoughts about the true nature of the world of men and the multiple nature of the search for peace. The ferment of doubt is at work among scientists, and one by one they will find ways of expressing it; and this time they will speak out as ordinary men and they will not try to trade on their credentials in the wholly different world of scientific endeavor.

II

Just as the atomic scientists gave a great impetus to the notion of a Single Solution to war, so they also were the ones whose achievements ironically have led to publicly supported scientific programs so huge and out of balance that the integrity of science itself sometimes seems compromised.

The production of the atomic bomb was a great big "scientific success story." Here the scientists were given a blank check; and they "delivered," with world-shaking results. With such credentials, the atomic scientists were in a commanding position. The doors of the Treasury swung open and the money poured out. For the physicist who had waited for years to test his theories on equipment too expensive for anyone to buy, it was a dream come true. National laboratories were established, universities were liberally supplied with scholarships and grants, and the university research work of scientists was greatly expanded by government contract.

Science was once a lonely search. A man, alone, struggled with ideas. His laboratory equipment was often humble and improvised, as was the great Rutherford's at Cavendish. (One scientist said of Rutherford's laboratory that "it looked like the inside of a garage.") Now the team is the mode. Good scientists have refused university appointments except on the condition that they bring certain of their colleagues with them!

The giant machines often far outshadow the men and their scientific ideas, symbolically and in fact. The multimillion dollar atom-smasher, designed to find new elementary particles, further inflates the prestige of those who find the search for these particles science's top priority. But the search for new knowledge of the very basics of *life* itself—the recent brilliant progress in working out the genetic code, for example—involves not billion dollar machines but original and creative minds, so for the time being apparently this revolutionary area of discovery must take an inferior rank. There are many scientists and medical men who find this order of priority quite incomprehensible.

Over the years the liberal patronage extended to

physics has extended to other areas of physical science and technology. The effect is that scientists have found themselves more and more firmly bound to specific programs: to invent and produce a given weapons system, and to turn out all sorts of other gadgets to strengthen the nation's defense (or propaganda) posture, or to strengthen the interservice competitive standing of the Air Force, the Navy, or the Army, and the prosperous industrial contractors who are at once their patrons and their pipeline to the public treasury. A similar process is at work in government programs in the life sciences.

The classic picture of the scientist as a creative *individual*, a man obsessed, working alone through the night, a man in a laboratory pursuing an idea—this has changed. Now scientists are ranked in platoons. They are organization men. In many cases the independent and humble search for new truths about nature has become confused with the bureaucratic impulse to justify expenditure and see that next year's budget is bigger than last's. Science is fast becoming a "hot" stock market item, a "growth stock." The vested interest in a project and its funds has more and more dominated the scientist's life and motivation.

The dire consequences to the vitality of science itself that threatens us has been stated by many distinguished scientists, among them Dr. Caryl P. Haskins, head of the Carnegie Institution of Washington, in the magazine *Science** for April 12, 1963. Dr. Haskins is by temperament and training not given to overstatement; his words therefore contain a warning not to be ignored.

"In the past," he wrote, "we have owed some of the greatest advances in our understanding of nature—not to mention the greatest leaps in technical exploitation—to the work of individual genius ill-fitted to the kind of specific scientific commitment that faces us on such a colossal scale today. It would be strange if the potential of such individuals in the years to come were less than it has been in the past. Indeed, it ought to be yet greater. . . .

"But what part of this priceless resource is annually swept irrevocably into the maw of activities organized about sharply committed goals? What part is annually consigned, at a formative age, to an environment which, while it may produce worthy scientific citizens, may also extinguish the full reach of their potentials? These are very serious questions indeed. . . ."

The space program happens at the moment to be the most extensive illustration of what has happened to science through its absorption into a fast-building and gargantuan establishment. Here the goals of the program are not scientific goals; they are political. This is not to say that the goals are therefore not justifiable, though whether they are is a serious question indeed.

* *Science* is the journal of the American Association for the Advancement of Science.

The space program merely illustrates how the direction of scientific effort now is no longer controlled by recognizable *scientific* considerations.

The scientists in these programs have a fearful choice. They are guests at a tax-supported feast of plenty. If they want money to test their ideas, to achieve prominence in their specialties, to earn more than a university pays, or merely to stay in the main current of what is happening in their fields, they must remain at the table. To reassert their traditional function as scholarly men they may cut themselves off from the big laboratories, the elaborate equipment, and the generous stipends. As a matter of fact, it is not unlikely that the day may come when it will be impossible for certain categories of scientists to make even this depressing choice. To be a scientist at all may come to mean being a scientist who is in a program that would not exist without tax-fund support and public—that is, political—goals.

III

The implications of this luxuriant growth of *public* science, which essentially began with the Atom, have set up deep tensions within the scientific community and particularly within the universities. Many scientists bitterly resent any suggestion that the great public outpouring of funds and programs since Hiroshima has been a mixed blessing. They insist, sometimes stridently, that the scientist is free, that "science is science." And yet many scientists and educators are wondering. Some university leaders speak out about a "lack of balance" in these programs. But when a third or half or more of a great university's funds come from government sources, the muffled tones some university officials use in discussing the issue is understandable.

The directors of the programs too, including university presidents, are insistent on this crucial point, that science is untainted. I am sure that most of them, not all, are persuaded that the basic purposes of education have not been compromised, and their opinion must be respected, but questioned. To them the danger is that government, as a patron, will sooner or later start ordering the scientists to produce certain predetermined results. One highly influential man of responsible experience both in university and government life, McGeorge Bundy, has recently argued that the federal dollar is "cleaner," so to speak, than almost all of the traditional sources of academic support, such as alumni gifts or foundation grants.

Mr. Bundy's point may well be valid, and yet there is something a little dated about it. Does anyone really expect the kind of gross and obvious governmental interference in university affairs that is the old-fashioned bogey of federal support?

What should concern us is something more subtle—and dangerous. Government support of university operations is now massive. These huge programs are tied in with a complex of patently nonacademic research and hardware operations conducted for corporations, government departments, defense and space projects of all descriptions. Federal money is not just one source of funds, and one claimant on scarce scientific talent. It is in many cases the *chief* support, and by all odds the *dominant* claimant. Most of the money and brains go into scientific and technological work that is largely unconnected with the principal functions of a university: teaching and research. *This* is the issue to which we should address ourselves.

Just as the engulfment of science in giant programs is threatening the independent functioning of scientists, so the very purpose of the university is under a serious challenge. So quickly has this challenge arisen that it is difficult to do much more now than to recognize it as one that must be faced, not ignored.

Let me cite one case out of my own experience that illustrates how remote from the basic purposes of a university some of the involvement of universities with government programs has become. The case also illustrates, I think, that we are dealing here with forces which need to be critically re-examined rather than with misguided or badly motivated individuals either in the universities or the government.

When I became Chairman of the civilian Atomic Energy Commission, my associates and I made a visit to the University of California. We knew that during the war the Manhattan Project had persuaded the University of California, for reasons of patriotism alone, to enter into a contract whereby the Los Alamos, New Mexico, operation of the Manhattan Project should be a contractual responsibility of the University of California. It was at Los Alamos that under the administrative and technical leadership of Dr. Robert Oppenheimer an extraordinary group of scientists was assembled; these men devised a workable nuclear weapon, tested it, and produced the only two atomic bombs ever used, the ones that devastated the cities of Hiroshima and Nagasaki.

Neither The Regents nor the officers of the University of California were permitted access to Los Alamos during the war. When the new civilian Commission called on The Regents, we found them anxious to be relieved of a contractual obligation which in peacetime they could not justify as an academic, or scholarly, or teaching, or research function of the University of California. I urged The Regents to continue that contract. One of my principal practical reasons was that the men at Los Alamos, both administrators and scientists, were insistent that they continue to be identified as members of the University of California faculty and staff. As a condition of remaining in the nonacademic, nonscholarly activities at Los Alamos, so essential to our national security, most of these scientists and administrators regarded it as essential that their status be that of members of the faculty and staff of a university that rarely saw them, as teachers or researchers.

77

In addition to Los Alamos, the University of California later took contractual responsibility for the establishment at Livermore, California, of the so-called hydrogen bomb program, and later still, a bomb testing site and operation in Nevada. The scientists and administrators in these three operations—Los Alamos, Livermore, and the Nevada test site—continue to be identified as part of the University of California. These operations run into very large sums of money and personnel, representing a substantial part of the total budget of the entire University of California at Berkeley.

But the question must be asked: what substantial addition to the role of the University of California in basic research, in scholarly work, and in the atmosphere of a university, do these huge operations at Los Alamos, Livermore, and the Nevada test site represent? Is it the function of a great university to have on its rolls, as teachers and administrators, individuals such as those at Los Alamos, Livermore, and the Nevada test site whose functions are so remote from and so largely unrelated to teaching and research?

Here is one case of many in which a university found itself deeply involved in essentially a nonuniversity function, not because it was grasping for funds but because it was appealed to on the grounds of patriotism. A university became heavily involved with government not because government sought to pervert the purposes of the university or dominate its academic functions. And yet because the trend that this repre-

78

sented was not seriously opposed, and re-examined, the University of California is burdened with a huge operation which I suggest is more properly the function of a nonuniversity agency. While I was AEC Chairman, I had great doubts about this trend, though on practical grounds at times there seemed no immediate alternative. So when a new bomb establishment was to be set up near Los Alamos, instead of asking the University of California to add this to its Los Alamos contract, I persuaded the Bell Telephone System to take this contractual responsibility, which it discharged very successfully. So, at the Oak Ridge operation of AEC, I urged that the University of Chicago (which had administered the Laboratory during the War) be replaced by Union Carbide, an industrial organization skilled in administering scientific and technical undertakings.

I suggest that there definitely are other ways of administering government programs than to put them upon the backs of universities, thereby running the risk of obscuring and perhaps injuring the function for which universities truly exist, which is education, research, and the creation of an atmosphere of scholarship and of inquiry. Surely we are courageous enough to face this issue: surely we are ingenious enough to see to it that great government programs can be carried out without this impairment of the function of the institutions of higher learning.

Here, then, are three of many questions that are

raised by this great expansion of universities into areas that lie outside of their traditional responsibility:

(1) To what extent has the teaching function of the universities been impaired by these extracurricular projects?

(2) To what extent has the independent function of scholarly research been overwhelmed and downgraded by the massive programitis that now so deeply absorbs many universities' attention?

(3) If these nonacademic projects do constitute a serious threat to the true purpose of the universities, at a time when the demands of a mounting student population are rising sharply, what can be done to relieve the burden? What projects can be shunted out of the universities to federal agencies or to private industry? Or, contrarily, if some universities are too deeply committed, should they take the further step of lopping off entirely what has become the minor function of teaching, and let new universities be established for that essential purpose?

Some educators and scientists are becoming more and more aware of what has been happening. They are showing signs of being much disturbed about it, and they should be. It is time this issue underwent a searching revaluation, initiated by the universities themselves, and by the scientists who have no small share of responsibility for these problems.

The fallibility and at times the innocence in human

affairs which many scientists have demonstrated is by no means restricted to them alone. Now we hear other voices, from the so-called social sciences, often cozily clubbed together in government-financed "corporations" or "institutes," or as soloists attached to universities. Their prestige as well as income derives largely from their role as seers who by gazing into their crystal ball of "empirical inquiry" find therein reason to support strategic doctrines that are pleasing to the then prevailing views of the government Establishment.

These "strategists" are now saying, in triumph: "The physical scientists have had their innings, now it's *our* turn for the big grants and the big prestige; it's our turn to show that we have the real answer to the process of thinking about peace and war."

Some of these latter-day oracles produce discussion and even thought that is stimulating and therefore useful, but anyone who has himself been responsible for decisions in a critical government post will, I dare say, find the gyrations of these analysts other-worldly.

Now if some of these exercises were for the sheer pleasure of such intellectual ping-pong, there would be less cause to object, even though the game is played at public expense. But one day this form of intellectual gymnastics may be put to use by some hard-pressed administrator or commander, in which case all of us might suffer irreparably.

I offer a sample or two from the works of one regarded as a leading practitioner of the military analysis school, Dr. Herman Kahn, head of the Hudson Institute, a "policy research organization," and as such a paid adviser to the United States Government.

As a stimulus to thinking, Dr. Kahn and his colleagues devise what they call the "scenario," a story that serves to call attention "to the large range of possibilities that must be considered in strategic analysis" of the kind he believes in. The *purpose* of analysis, to one who is a decision-maker, should be something useful in the process of making decisions affecting, in this case, the life and death of millions.

There are those who criticize these fictional plots, Dr. Kahn observes with great good temper, on the ground that they "may be so divorced from reality as to be not only useless but misleading and therefore dangerous. However, one must remember that the scenario is not used as a predictive device. . . . *It is hard to see how there can be a divorce from a reality which does not exist.*" (My italics)

Here is one example of the scenario method, from a recent book by Dr. Kahn:*

A thermonuclear war, so this scenario reads, has been fought; on the day after "the war is over" the President of the United States sends to Premier Khrushchev "a well-known book on possible constitutional forms for world government, *World Peace*

* *Thinking about the Unthinkable*, p. 148 et seq., Horizon Press, New York, 1962.

82

Through World Law."** With the book goes a message from the President: "There's no point in your reading this book; you will not like it any more than I did. I merely suggest you sign it, right after my signature. This is the only plan which has been even roughly thought through; let us therefore accept it." How such a technique stimulates the imagination *usefully* I confess I have difficulty in comprehending, but since Congress provides government funds to Dr. Kahn's Hudson Institute and others, for this method of stimulating thought, Congressmen and military men presumably find some merit in it.

A recent plug for operational analysis methods in human affairs comes from Dr. Albert Wohlstetter of The RAND Corporation, in an article appearing in the stately pages of *Foreign Affairs*.

Dr. Wohlstetter is contemptuous of the claim of Sir Charles Snow and other physical scientists that they have a science-induced "intuition" about the human choices by which it is determined "whether we live or die." Standing atop the prestige of The RAND Corporation, which is largely supported by government contracts, he cites the superiority of his own "behavioral sciences" over the superman claims of some scientists because he and his school of thought are actually engaged in "empirical study of military operations likely in a nuclear war."

To ascertain the content of such "empirical study"

** By Grenville Clark and Louis B. Sohn, Harvard University Press, Cambridge, Mass., 1958.

the outsider must consult the unclassified activities and publications of the behaviorist-strategists. For example, so Dr. Kahn informs us, for a week a group of these specialists played "war and peace games." The following is a portion of Dr. Kahn's summary of this exercise in playmanship.* (His books are full of other even more precious samples.)

A nuclear weapon explodes at a Strategic Air Command site near Mobile, killing 50,000 Americans. What to do? After much confusion—among the players at least—"the President," Dr. Kahn reports, "decides upon expedient action. He orders the manufacture of false evidence that the Soviets produced the explosion. This framed evidence is strong, but not conclusive. Unfortunately for its credibility, several newspapers at this point print a letter sent to them and postmarked before the Mobile explosion. It is signed by an air force officer assigned to the SAC base at Mobile who has disappeared. This letter states that the writer intends to cause an explosion to show the world how dangerous the current situation is. He hopes by this means to bring peace on earth. It is then discovered that the writer had been active in Communist front organizations some fifteen years earlier and that this had not been caught by the security system.

"At this point it is clear that the truth about the explosion and about possible Russian responsibility is

* *Ibid.*, p. 159 et seq.

never likely to be found." And so forth; the other "games" reported are about of the same tenor.

Such exercises and stream-of-consciousness cerebration about public policy and decision-making, engaged in with such zest and confidence by these experts, is certainly not without value, if for no other reason than the controversy they engender over their usefulness to anyone responsible for human affairs. But the matter is more serious than this: the good name of science is invoked in support of such empiricism. The RAND "conflict-systems studies" are identified by no less a practitioner than Dr. Wohlstetter as "simply the *application of the methods of science* to the analysis of political military strategy alternatives."

More than science's good name may be at stake, for all those ordinary intelligent laymen who are outside the Establishment may know. The methods of our defense, the billions for particular weapons systems, the conscripting of our young men may be among the consequences of these exotic vagaries.

Of course the Answers of this new expertise will be just as misleading as those of their competitors of whom they are so scornful, the physical scientists, although the jargon they use is even more vaporish and impenetrable. We have nothing to gain merely by substituting a new kind of specialist expertise applied to human emotions and human institutions.

These new seers usually disavow that they are seeking "answers," and on this shifty basis ink up the waters of responsibility like a startled squid. But the men for whom these "empirical studies" are prepared *are* seeking answers. That is their job; otherwise they would not be commissioning these studies. When the Secretary of Defense takes a position on military and diplomatic strategy he must sit by the hour before Congressional committees or in press conferences and justify that position for the laymen on that committee or among the press. Members of Congress and the national press have the function to ask questions for the rest of us. But to what extent are decisions of a Secretary of Defense (or of State) about nuclear weapons or missiles or the NATO Alliance's nuclear force based on the thinking of experts outside the government service whom no one knows except when they choose to write a book or appear on a TV panel? Could these research analysts in human affairs stand up to the kind of questions a Congressional committee or a tough press would ask? Does the Congress actually know what goes on in this labyrinth of expertise? These questions need attention.

There is no cause for alarm however, so long as men who have had actual experience in the decision-making ordeal are fully in charge and subject to public accountability. I find it refreshing to contrast this expertise with the manner of approaching the decisional function of such a man as General Lauris Norstad, formerly Supreme Commander in Europe; or of the mental-emotional perspective of the Chairman of the Senate Committee on Foreign Affairs, Senator J. William Fulbright or that of President Kennedy in the Cuban missile crisis, or General Eisenhower on D-day, or General Lucius Clay in the earlier Soviet squeeze on Berlin.

Unfortunately we may have great difficulty in coming to grips with these experts. They are paid by us, from our taxes, but they are not accountable to us or to Congress in the same way as are government employees, such as Generals or Secretaries of Defense. For the most part, they are shielded from public view by being employees of so-called "private" corporations which operate predominately on government contracts. In substance I wonder why they are any different from direct federal employees as to responsibility, and yet they are freed from the accountability—and the salary limitations—of those who are in direct federal service. I can think of few things that over a decade can be more demoralizing to the strength and dignity of the federal career service than this: the creation and proliferation of a body of super civil servants, men who perform governmental functions yet who are independent of government and its obligations, men recruited and paid and supervised as if they were in private employment, but actually doing the government's work. For they are virtually immune from the tough, essential, and distinguishing characteristic of democratic processes of public life, the essence of

87

which is direct accountability, in the open air, to public lay scrutiny.

For this strange distortion of democratic principles, in a sense, the Atom is the source. The Atom led the way in the vast outpouring of public money, of programs and projects on a huge scale; now it is not hard to see why other groups of experts are following that honeyed trail, determined to get their share too.

We need a better definition and understanding of the roles of the various skills and specializations on which we depend so much. We know how well these specialists can perform in their own fields, but how much do they have to offer on the human questions that transcend specialization?

I find it interesting that this confusion about the direct applicability to human affairs of scientific or technical special knowledge or method is not confined by any means to scientists and technicians of the West. The Soviet scientists seem to have been snared in the same delusion. On May 22, 1963, Dr. Igor Y. Tamm, a Nobel laureate in physics, speaking in America, urged a "bold experiment" *in politics*, comparable to the experiments in the physical sciences by which Dr. Tamm had synthesized the theories of relativity and quantum mechanics.

Such misconceptions of the limits of specialized and scientific knowledge and method when applied to human affairs are a serious disservice to science. Happily, many scientists, including distinguished scientists with whom I have worked as a layman, have as human beings, apart from their scientific genius, every bit as much knowledge of human affairs as any other comparable group of men. But no more.

The process we are caught up in, a spiral of conflicting and misapplied expertise, contains this danger: that the true value and function of the various bodies of knowledge will become blurred by confusion and debased with doubts. For this dilemma the scientific community bears a considerable responsibility. The scientists—by no means all, of course, but many— were among the first to suggest that the imagination and skills required in one special area could be successfully employed in dealing with the problems of mankind. This implied superiority of expertise was given a famous slogan: the "two cultures" of Sir Charles Snow. It is the kind of provocative idea that make one wonder. Are there really "two cultures"? Is there really something so special about the life and training of a scientist that makes him more competent than other men to cope with the whole of things on earth?

Scientists have performed, perhaps not deliberately, a most useful function in that they have stimulated a re-examination of the values of society as a whole. Sir Charles Snow's notion about the "two cultures" and the superiority of the scientist, and the replies of those scientists who disagree with Snow, have had the not inconsiderable virtue of forcing us to think hard and specifically about the role of science in our world, and indeed about the nature of man.

The current re-examination of science and the role of scientists will have a positive and wholesome consequence. It, will serve, I think, to substitute a rugged lay skepticism in the place of an unquestioning acquiescence in the all-wisdom of the scientist and the technical man. To be skeptical about the all-wisdom of technical people is not to be against technical knowledge; it is to *be aware of how human are these fellow men called experts*. It is the skepticism of the nonscientist and nontechnical man that may be our chief bulwark against an intellectually arrogant neotechnocracy that is disdainful of those who do not have the equipment and the jargon of expertise.

The instances in which scientists have been positive and cocksure one day and reverse themselves a month or a year later are legion. And they range all the way from the absurd ups and downs of conclusions about the effect of exploding a nuclear bomb in the so-called Van Allen radiation belt to the question of a permissible human tolerance to insecticides, and to radical reversals among physicians as to how to raise healthy babies. These instances are part of the layman's everyday experience.

Are scientists somehow different from the rest of us? To put it facetiously: Are scientists human beings?

After years of working with them, I know that scientists *are* human beings, in the broadest and warmest sense of the term. And similarly, for myself I have concluded that the concept of a special virtue in the making of a scientist, a virtue that gives him an advantage in handling human affairs, is rarely justified. The scientists themselves have given us in the past decade and a half, when they have been in the center of the stage, a wonderful and imaginative demonstration of this. They have proven beyond all doubt that they are human, and nothing more admiring could be said. They have shown us that they can be just as wise and just as foolish, just as judicious and just as ridiculous, just as clear-headed and just as bone-headed, as any of us laymen can ever be.

CHAPTER VI

―○―

WHATEVER HAPPENED TO
THE PEACEFUL ATOM?

A FEW DAYS before Christmas of 1945 a young Senator from Connecticut, Brian McMahon, introduced a bill which some eight months later was enacted into law and is known as the McMahon Act. The introductory words of this bill expressed a common conviction: that a revolutionary period based upon the peaceful use of atomic discoveries lay just ahead. I quote from the Congressional Declaration of Policy of the McMahon Act:

"The effect of the use of atomic energy for civilian purposes upon the social, economic and political structures of today cannot now be determined. It is reasonable to anticipate, however, that *tapping this new source of energy will cause profound changes in our present way of life.*"

The Declaration then concludes: "Accordingly it is hereby declared to be the policy of the people of the United States that the development and utilization of atomic energy shall be directed toward improving the public welfare, increasing the standard of living, strengthening free competition among private enterprises so far as is practicable, and cementing world peace."

A year later almost to the day, in the mid-afternoon of December 31, 1946, I was in President Truman's office in the White House with a group of my associates. I sat at the President's elbow as he signed a document that transferred from the Manhattan Project, as it was called, the complex of wartime atomic energy facilities of factories, laboratories, and weapons to the five-man Atomic Energy Commission of civilians. At midnight on that same day, General Leslie Groves, the forceful and dedicated Army officer who had carried the responsibility for producing the first atomic bomb, issued a farewell message which included these words: "Five years ago the idea of atomic power was only a dream. You of the Army's Manhattan Project have made that dream a reality. With regard to peaceful applications, you have raised the curtain on vistas of a new world."

These declarations of the McMahon Act and of General Groves' farewell message reflected quite accurately the expectations widely held in 1945 and 1946. American domestic policy and America's first efforts toward atomic disarmament, in which I participated, were erected on the foundation of just such expectations. I fully shared these views at that time, or I could not have with such conviction and intensity of effort joined in the work of trying to bring these expectations of a "new world" to reality, by the tapping of this new source of energy for civilian uses.

The preamble to the McMahon Act explicitly set out

the expectations and premises of 1946: we were on the threshold of a new source of energy believed to be revolutionary in its consequences. It is interesting to recall that the Russians expressed much the same euphoric expectations about atomic energy at that time.

On this explicit premise radical and unprecedented measures were adopted by the Congress and the people. It was because of these expectations that for the first time in our history a new technical development became a monopoly of government, its future entrusted not to normal competitive forces but to a single government agency, the Atomic Energy Commission, armed with billions of dollars and the broadest of powers. This was for America a radical step, and it was recognized as such. Nothing of this nature had ever been attempted in order to further other technical discoveries or inventions that did in fact revolutionize our way of life: the dynamo, the electric light, the automotive engine, the aeroplane, the radio tube.

We did this because of a conviction that there was an overriding national interest in development not of simply one more source of energy in a nation already so richly endowed in other sources of energy. No, this energy of the atom was given a special status and priority because it was expected to have a "profound effect on our way of life." *This* was the national interest that was thought to be at stake, that justified these extraordinary measures. It was *this* national interest that justified a prodigious scale of effort, unheard-of-expenditures of public money, fantastic absorption of a large portion of the scientific and technical and industrial resources of the nation.

Immediately after President Truman signed the executive order transferring the wartime properties of the Manhattan District to the civilian Atomic Energy Commission, we proceeded to fortify and expand an already extensive atomic establishment. A good deal of this expansion and additional investment, indeed most of it, was attributable to research and production plants in order that atomic bombs could be improved in design and their production speeded.

The nonmilitary Atomic Energy Commission program also claimed a very great deal of attention and investment of many facilities and of human talents. The universities of the southeast were brought together in a great expansion of the Oak Ridge Institute and of the nonmilitary facilities at Oak Ridge. A similar program bringing in universities but emphasizing national laboratories has been carried out at the Argonne National Laboratory near Chicago, the Brookhaven National Laboratory on Long Island, the laboratory at the University of Iowa at Ames, the scientific complex in New Mexico, the laboratory and facilities at Berkeley. One could continue this tabulation even further.

Never has there been, anywhere in the world, so broad and generously financed an attack on the technical and economic problems of bringing a new scientific discovery into the realm of application and of widespread use. This prodigious effort was predicated on the belief and hope that this great new source of energy for mankind could produce results as dramatically and decisively beneficial to man as the bomb was dramatically destructive.

The scale of effort today continues unabated. The AEC is actually pressing for a new program, to cost two billion dollars over a decade. Not just improvements in existing reactors, but a whole new line of technology, the so-called breeder reactor, is now being boomed, with predictions ranging from nebulous to conservative. The initial goal that was the justification both for the unique status given the peaceful Atom and the gargantuan scale of public expenditure has long since been proved to be a mirage; so much so that the custodians of the Atom, the AEC and the Joint Congressional Committee, not only prefer to forget that this justification has proved a mirage but take to task those who, like myself, remind the country of that fact. But it was this "revolutionary" source of energy expected from the peaceful atom that was the original justification, as the McMahon Act preamble says quite explicitly and accurately. That myth of a revolution continues to be fed by the American taxpayer. Private firms repeat this fiction at this late day, as part of institutional promotion of the sale of their atomic reactors.

In a full page advertisement appearing in April 1963, North American Aviation Corporation pictures an American papa, mama, and the kids at their family dinner, with the big caption: ONE OF THE MOST REVOLUTIONARY EVENTS OF THE 20TH CENTURY JUST HAPPENED IN THIS ROOM. In smaller type this "revolutionary event" is explained: "Just a moment ago the peaceful atom started supplying electric power that lights this room. The room looks no different than before; yet the world is far brighter as a result. For the atom has proved itself an answer to man's growing need for electric power."

But in human affairs, including politics and civil service as well as business, a vested interest in a shattered illusion is a commonplace. To have second thoughts in the pursuit of a will-of-the-wisp in public programs or in private enterprise takes moral courage and aroused taxpayers or stockholders.

In the 1940's it was reasonable to join in General Groves' and Senator McMahon's view of the possibility of a "new world" that peaceful applications of atomic energy might bring. Responsible men spoke of atomic power so cheap it wouldn't pay to meter it. Most of us were less exuberant by far, yet even those with a less euphoric outlook had ample grounds to believe that the expectations of the 'forties should be given a hard try.

But does what made sense in 1946 still make sense today? This is what we should consider.

97

Suppose in 1946, when the McMahon Act was passed, Congress had been told what we now know but did not know then: that if you will vest great powers in a special and unique government agency, the Atomic Energy Commission, if you build great research and development laboratories all over the country, explore for, find and buy uranium here and abroad, subsidize the costs of uranium fuel, bear large development costs and part of capital costs for manufacturers of electric equipment and utilities—if you do these things at the cost of billions of dollars for twenty or thirty years the country will have a new source of civilian electricity that is just as good and costs no more than what would be produced without the AEC, without these facilities and expenditures? What would Congress have said? My guess is that the Congress and the people would have gone to any lengths for military objectives of the Atom, such as weapons and the submarine, but would have said "nothing doing" on such a prospectus for peaceful civilian electricity.

Even in those early days the AEC general advisory committee, a group of eminent men, uttered words of caution about this new world. Industrialists like Philip Sporn reminded the country and the scientific community that power from the Atom is like any other power, that the Atom is just another kind of fuel and not a magic short-cut to almost costless electricity. But for the most part these voices were not heeded.

A great satirist, Frank Sullivan, had a very good

time kidding the clichés of exuberance of those days. Some of you will remember the "testimony," in question and answer form, of Frank Sullivan's creation, the cliché expert, Mr. Arbuthnot. Here are a few excerpts from Mr. Sullivan's piece entitled "The Cliché Expert Testifies on the Atom," published in 1946.*

From the witness stand Mr. Arbuthnot told his examiner that he'd better learn to use the words "harness and unleash" if he expected to talk about the Atom. "They are two words frequently used. With pea, of course."

Q. "Why pea?

A. "Oh, everything is in terms of the pea. You know how much U-235 it would take to drive a car to the moon and back?

Q. "No, sir. How much?

A. "A lump the size of a pea.

Q. "You wouldn't settle for a lump the size of a radish or a bean?

A. "Sorry. The pea is the accepted vegetable in these explanations. . . ."

Reading some current atomic power predictions the colloquy with the cliché expert, if Mr. Sullivan will look the other way, might continue in this way:

Q. "After seventeen years, where are we in 1963, Mr. Arbuthnot?

A. "Threshold. That is the correct cliché today. We are on the threshold of cheap atomic power. You'll

* From *A Rock in Every Snowball*, Little, Brown and Company, Boston, 1946.

have to learn that word if you expect to be an atomic expert, my friend.

Q. "But didn't you, in 1954, testify that we were then on the 'threshold.' And then again in 1960, didn't you say the same thing?

A. "Yes, of course I did. Threshold it was and threshold is still the correct cliché.

Q. "And how high is that threshold in 1963?

A. "High? Oh, the same height as in 1954. Hundreds of millions of dollars a year high.—Breeder.

Q. "Breeder, Mr. Arbuthnot? This is a mixed audience and I'll ask you to watch your language.

A. "Take it easy. Breeder, that's the newest atomic cliché. When you get asked hard questions about the old-fashioned atomic power plant, just say 'breeder' and you're off the hook, because a breeder atomic plant is in the future, so who can dispute the forecasts? You'll learn this atomic cliché thing yet, my friend."

The ease with which Mr. Sullivan made fun of the clichés of 1948 may have indicated that there was more than a little puffing in the build-up of atomic energy. It might be useful—and fun—if Mr. Sullivan turned his considerable talents for satire loose on some of the purple clichés about the "space age," current successor to the atomic "new world."

Today no one expects or even predicts that some magic of technology will be found whereby electricity from the Atom can be produced so cheaply and abundantly as to "cause profound changes in our present way of life." Somewhere along the line the goal has shifted, except in the promotional literature and rhetoric. Now the objective is a quite different one: to try to produce atomic electricity that is or will be *just as good* as electricity from coal, oil, or falling water; or to use more formal language, "competitive," meaning competitive in cost.

Even those who laid their technical reputations on the line, and who made enthusiastic predictions of a few years ago, are becoming disenchanted, as the new technical obstacles and the cost of overcoming them become apparent. A press association dispatch of May 18, 1962 reports that Admiral Hyman Rickover, "advised Congress to make an initial investment in a big 500,000 kilowatt nuclear power plant—but not with the idea that it would produce economically competitive power. . . ." Admiral Rickover's testimony, the account continues, "was in contrast to glowing predictions given to the Committee in the past about proposed atomic power plants." In the light of these past predictions it showed the moral courage that is characteristic of the Admiral for him to testify, as reported, that civilian atomic power reactors "should not be built for any other purpose than to learn something." It would be "a waste of government funds," he said, "just to go out and build a big reactor."

I said that the goal now is electric power that is "just as good." But the potential hazards to life and health of hundreds of thousands of people in densely populated areas adjacent to power plants (such as that projected in the heart of New York City) make it far from accurate to label atomic power plants "just as good" as conventional power plants, even should the cost ultimately be virtually the same, or even less. In the event of accidents, human error, or sabotage, such atomic plants certainly present greater hazards than conventional power plants. It is expecting a good deal to get a disinterested appraisal of these hazards from the manufacturers who have these atomic power plants to sell, or from the AEC and the Joint Committee of Congress since they are committed to a nation-wide atomic power program.

The insurance industry of the United States refused to provide complete insurance against so widespread a potential peril to human life and property damage as an atomic power plant presents. So the federal government, by special statute, now underwrites most of the public catastrophe aspects of these hazards. No such insurance problem exists as to nonatomic power plants, of course. The ethics of equating risk to human life and health with dollars of tax-supported insurance coverage has aroused considerable misgivings.

Atomic power plants inevitably produce a by-product that is furiously radioactive. After all these years, no way safely to dispose of these waste poisons has been demonstrated on full scale, or to handle them at processing plants, or to transport them with complete safety from power plants or processing areas to a burial ground. The underground storage of these deadly and now massive wastes continues to constitute a potential source of danger to the population, and it is a source of considerable added expense as compared to the ashes of a conventional thermal electricity plant.

So "just as good" is far from the whole story. But except for these greater perils of radiation poisoning, hard to measure precisely because so much is yet to be learned about radiation, one could earnestly hope atomic electricity would prove in time to be "competitive" or nearly so, *as to cost*, with energy from other sources. If the only way we could provide for our rising energy needs were these still experimental operations, we might have to take such long risks. But the split atom is but one way to provide *heat* with which to turn turbines and generators. There are many other ways: the burning of coal, lignite, gas, and oil. The split atom produces a still most inadequately understood phenomenon, massive radiation, and it is the radiation that provides the heat. Burning oil, gas or coal provides heat without poisonous radiation.

The story of the second coming of coal as a source of energy in the past ten years is a good illustration of how difficult it is to predict a specific change on a long-range basis. To nearly everyone's surprise the cost of electricity from coal has been drastically reduced in recent years and is continuing to be further reduced. And the reserves of coal in locations that modern technology makes economic are ample for a very considerable period.

Coal is not glamorous, like the Atom or water power. It is a very humble source of electricity. The coal industry for two generations was called a "sick industry." For a long time technical advances in mining and transporting coal at lower cost and of producing electricity from the heat of burning coal advanced hardly at all in an economic sense. In the mysterious way by which changes take place at the most unexpected places, suddenly coal in the last decade has made enormous strides.

The predictions about coal and oil have been notoriously wrong. Take but one, that of a British scientist, Dr. P. M. S. Blackett; writing in 1948 he said, "America's fuel reserves are only likely to be adequate in the future *at steeply rising costs*." This proved to be off the beam by 180 degrees. Actually the proven reserves have increased, and thermal electric generating costs have declined steeply and continue to decline.

Today improved technology and economics in the mining of coal and its transportation, greater efficiency in the transformation of coal's heat into electricity (thirty per cent increased efficiency in a few years) and in long-distance power transmission, have made coal in many parts of the country, including the industrial Ohio Valley, by all odds the least costly source of energy except for some of the better water-power sites. The United States' supply of coal, brought in reach of markets by new methods of mining and transportation of coal and of transmitting electricity, is more than adequate for many decades, to meet the mounting energy needs of this country. Mine-mouth coal, with transmission line inter-ties, is establishing new low records of cost, and the costs continue still to be downward.

If the continued huge expenditures of government funds and technical brains for atomic development is for the purpose of establishing whether uranium as a fuel is, or will be, less or more costly than coal even by a mill or so per unit of electricity, in itself a desirable goal, is there a *national public interest* that justifies this scale of effort? Where there is no present or prospective economic need for a product or service, does it make sense for the government of the United States to continue to spend as much as it does on civilian atomic energy? I doubt this. Military applications, including the nuclear submarine power plant, stand in a different category, of course.

Does it make sense for some of America's ablest technical men in the AEC, its contractors, and in industry to confront frustration after frustration for no presently foreseeable overriding public purpose? I think not.

So I submit two propositions:

(1) The problems of securing safe and competitively economic power from the Atom have greatly

exceeded the technical experts' and administrators' expectations.

(2) Other sources of power are ample and diminishing in cost.

If we accept these two propositions we will have a new perspective for sensible public discussion and decision. The conclusion could save vast sums of government funds; a great deal of scientific and technical talent could then be used in other areas.

When the economics of power show a need for atomic energy when compared with the costs and lack of risks of radiation dangers of other sources of energy, the *manufacturers of equipment and the utility industry, private and public, will supply that need without government prodding.*

It was not only a major economic source of heat and power that those vast expenditures on atomic energy were intended to secure. It was believed that atomic discoveries would produce revolutionary advances not only in basic science but in their application in medicine and in the growing of food and fibre, a revolutionary contribution to the conquest of poverty and disease on a world-wide scale.

Radioactive isotopes have indeed been a great boon as a tool of science. Those who in the 'forties sensed that this might well be the greatest benign use of atomic energy have thus far been proven right. The radioactive isotope has had important though still limited applications in medicine and in a few other areas such as chemical engineering.

As to industrial applications, though, a new and realistic note of prudence is emerging. The Dow Chemical Company, for example, recently announced its success in using a radioactive substance, cobalt 60, as a catalyst to produce small quantities of the organic compound ethyl bromide. The headline was of the style of the old exuberant era: "The Atom runs a chemical plant." But in the fine print the company's chemist said, "It's just another type of catalyst, another tool to consider. Ultraviolet light and chemical agents may still be the best, most economical way to produce many chemicals." The Atom in chemistry is now seen to be a part of the mainstream of chemistry, not a kind of magic.

There continues to be a very high level of intellectual excitement and progress in physics, following the path cut a generation ago by such giants as the late Niels Bohr and his younger creative counterparts. The money and brains devoted to nuclear science apart from research and development for atomic power have, I think, on the whole been well spent; but I am not alone in questioning whether so large a part of our total resources of brains as is devoted to this one area of science is justified *compared* with the opportunities in other scientific fields.

We can well be proud—I certainly am—of our great atomic laboratories, in the establishment of several of which I had some direct responsibility. But should we assume that they *always* must expand, that they will never be cut back in favor of other kinds of research? A kind of Parkinson's Law of Research has developed: that research expands as fast as money for that work is made available. Fifteen billions of dollars of federal funds for research could become thirty billions if we don't take a hard look at Parkinson's Law of Research soon.

The Atomic Energy Commission continues to stockpile uranium. By 1966, we are told, there will be a *surplus* of uranium over needs for weapons and reactors of a value of a billion dollars. Do the prospects for atomic reactors in the coming decade justify such a surplus reserve? If not, can we afford to build a kind of atomic political pork barrel, or a uranium Congressional bloc like the silver bloc?

There are various reasons why we continue to do these things in the face of the reduced prospects that atomic power will have a profound effect on American life. Some are straight political ones. Some stem from the natural and justifiable pride of men whose technical careers have been given over to this goal and who have understandable difficulty being wholly objective about the results. But deeper still, I think, are the remnants of a resolve that we *must* prove that the Atom has a present peaceful nonmilitary use of very great importance.

As first chairman of AEC and before that as one

of those who helped draft a State Department proposal for international control of the Atom, I had a share in formulating and popularizing that hope of peaceful potentials. But in the intervening years the hope has been considerably dimmed. The rhetoric and the emotion, however, linger on; the facts should be faced, for they will prevail.

Is the peaceful Atom then a gold-brick, a fiasco, a flop? No, nothing has changed the majesty of the basic discovery or its theoretical potential. The trouble is rather with ourselves for allowing our determination that the Atom should have a peaceful use to inflate our hopes so grossly. There are some who say that what we need is a revised timetable for the realization of these hopes. But in the meantime—and it may be many years—several other potential sources of energy and the improvement of existing sources may, as a consequence of the imperative of change, relegate atomic energy as a cost-competitive source of power to only specialized and limited applications.

Why were our hopes inflated?

The basic cause, I think was a conviction, and one that I shared fully, and tried to inculcate in others, that somehow or other the discovery that had produced so terrible a weapon simply *had* to have an important peaceful use. Such a sentiment is far from ignoble. We are a peace-loving people. Everyone, our leaders and laymen and scientists and military men, wanted to establish that there is a beneficial use of this great discovery. We were grimly determined to prove that this discovery was not just a weapon. This led perhaps to wishful thinking, a wishful elevation of the "sunny side" of the Atom. So we did not see atomic energy as just another form of heat, another fuel.

The strong attraction of the peaceful Atom as an offset to the terrors of the Atom's destructiveness as a weapon has led to some strange results.

Years ago the Russians announced that, unlike the bloodthirsty Americans who only thought of the Atom in terms of destruction, they, the Russians, were developing this explosive for peaceful purposes, such as great excavation for ports and the like. Most knowledgeable people at that time thought this was a characteristic piece of Soviet cold war propaganda, and obvious nonsense. Yet the pressure on us to prove that atomic weapons were not the only product of these great scientific efforts was such that our own atomic energy program has of late gone in for this kind of thing: projects for blowing out harbors, making explosions underground to produce steam, and so on. Without judging the details of these undertakings, the important thing they show is how far scientists and administrators will go to try to establish a nonmilitary use.

For example, dramatic pictures of a great hole blasted out in the desert by a "peaceful" atomic explosion in July 1962 were released to the press by AEC, for the first time, in November of that year. The release was at a time when the AEC's budget for this kind of "spectacular" was before the Budget Bureau. As a build-up for the peaceful use of the Atom, the amount of earth moved by this explosion in the desert was compared with the earth moved in digging a tunnel under New York's East River, where an atomic explosion would hardly be welcomed. This is just another of the many instances of the way in which public relations techniques—the not-so-hidden persuader—have been used to promote the appropriation of funds for the peaceful Atom.

Another consequence of this same kind of effort to glamorize the Atom is a foreign aid program within the Atomic Energy Commission, part of President Eisenhower's program in 1954 called "Atoms for Peace." An elaborate ritual for providing atomic research and reactor equipment and technology to Thailand and Guatemala and other underdeveloped countries became an expensive show-piece of the AEC program. Much of this was an utterly meaningless and wasteful operation, for most of these countries had hardly a cadre of scientists or the necessary facilities to put this "exchange" of atomic knowledge to any significant use. Even as a propaganda move it was self-defeating and naïve. A great many of these countries need and could use doctors and medicine, storage-batteries, plows and fertilizers and seed—and good *elementary* scientific instruction. Only the desire to prove somehow that Atoms were for peace could

111

justify the absurdity of a separate program, not in the foreign aid part of the State Department but in the AEC.

Let me cite another consequence of the "come-hither" of the peaceful Atom, overshadowing other equally promising areas of science. From the very beginning of the AEC it has been easier to get Congress to appropriate funds for science and research if somehow the Atom can be tacked on to the request. This is not to deprecate the importance of the huge accelerators, costing hundreds of millions of dollars, or the elaborate and even luxurious laboratories that have grown up at Oak Ridge, Argonne, Brookhaven, and Berkeley. But there are other claimants for research energies and prestige, such as medical research, and particularly biology.

I submit that it will not be possible for Congress to allocate appropriately the total brain and money resources of the country to be expended on scientific research and development so long as the Atom is thought of and dealt with not as one segment of scientific effort to be balanced against other segments, but as a thing apart. Until the Atom is brought back fully into the mainstream of the scientific effort of the country, as an element of that mainstream, Congress will continue to be vulnerable to special pleading for funds for atomic research with too little opportunity realistically to weigh that field against the needs and opportunities of other parts of science.

Of all our national resources, minds are the most important. Two-thirds of the trained minds available for exploring our scientific and technical frontiers are absorbed by the atomic energy and space and defense activities of our country. Let me emphasize that: *two-thirds.*

As a consequence, the rest of America's needs are relatively impoverished, neglected, and starved.

For the first time the country is beginning to realize that we cannot have a satisfactory economic growth rate if this two-thirds allocation of our trained brains goes on much longer. President Kennedy's economic report to Congress of December 21, 1962, has this comment to make: "We have," he said of this two-thirds absorption of trained minds, "paid a price by sharply limiting the scarce scientific and engineering resources available to the civilian sectors of the American economy."

The "civilian sectors" is a colorless economist's term for what it is that keeps America going. Cut off the research and technical blood supply to the "civilian sectors," and the space, defense and atomic energy programs will have no one left to pay their bills. Cutting back on this drain on scarce brains is not specifically proposed in the President's economic report, but I suggest Congress consider the atomic energy program as one good place to begin to cut back sharply, to make more brains available to some of the presently starved civilian areas of science and technology.

113

CHAPTER VII

——————————●○●——————————

ATOMIC ANACHRONISMS:

The Atomic Energy Commission and the Joint
Congressional Committee on Atomic Energy

ANACHRONISM: *Anything . . . that is incongruous in point of time with its surroundings. . . .*
WEBSTER'S NEW INTERNATIONAL DICTIONARY

IF WE ARE GOING to readjust our ideas about the
emphasis we ought to place on the peaceful Atom then
some plain talk is in order as to the functions of the
agency that has responsibility for it, the Atomic Energy
Commission. Surely the contours of its job should conform to the present picture of the Atom, not that of
1946 when the AEC was established.

It made good sense for Congress in 1946, with the
country's general approval, to set up a wholly separate
civilian agency for the Atom. At that time we *alone*
had the Bomb. We had committed ourselves to international control. We were sincerely attempting to
prove to the world that our intentions were peaceful.
Therefore, custody and control and development of
this terrible new force were placed in the hands of a
civilian agency—not the military. Collecting in a single
such civilian agency all of the functions relating to the
Atom seemed to be the best safeguard possible against
the loss of the scientific and technical secrets we and

the British together had in our possession. Atomic energy was generally expected to transform the face of industrial society within a short space of time, and therefore a special *new* agency was clearly needed to prepare and plan for such a dynamic change.

These reasons were certainly valid enough in 1946 and 1947. But how do they stand up in the light of the facts of today?

(1) First, the emphasis on a civilian agency.

The world is now and has been for some years in an atomic arms race. The hope of international control is dim. The military facts of the mid-'sixties now have forced us to place large quantities of nuclear arms directly in the hands of our military here and overseas—in the skies, in missiles beneath the earth's surface, under the seas.

We still have civilian control in the sense that the President, as always, is responsible, but the role of the AEC as a special civilian custodian and watchdog has evaporated.

The AEC functions chiefly as a designer, developer, maker, and tester of atomic weaponry. These grave technical responsibilities have been carried out with distinction by able men, but as the reason for a sharp separation between civilian and military atomic roles has faded, so the distinctive role of the AEC has changed. The AEC as weaponeer has in fact become very much a part of the military establishment, serving the needs and goals of that military establishment as

115

defined by the military. The spectrum of weapons and the range of war plans are now very broad indeed, from intercontinental missiles to conventional tools of the infantry or of guerrilla warfare. In so broad a context the AEC, expert in nuclear weaponry alone, can hardly provide an indispensable *independent* civilian judgment to the Chiefs of Staff. Realistically, the AEC essentially is not too different from any major technical contractor to the Defense Department in the area of missiles, say, or some other weapons system.

(2) The second premise on which the AEC was founded, that of technical secrecy, was greatly undermined in 1949, when Russia tested its first bomb. Atomic secrecy on technical matters still has some value to us, but since 1949 it has become progressively less crucial, first because we realized gradually that secrecy in basic science is a myth, and second because the variety of secrets (that is, of temporary technological advantages) has multiplied (in rocketry, in submarines, etc.) and is very far from being preponderant in the atomic field, as once had been the case. The function of the AEC as a gigantic strong-box for all the major US weapons secrets just does not jibe with the facts of today.

(3) The "New World" of atomic plenty, as reviewed earlier, does not exist. Certainly the energy of the peaceful Atom occupies only a subordinate role in shaping the economic development of the United States.

In sum, the three chief reasons for the establishment of the AEC in the late 'forties are no longer wholly valid in the world of the 'sixties. This is not to say that the AEC has "failed" and should be abolished. But however painful it may be to the pride and future hopes that have grown up within the AEC and the major industrial interests which depend upon it, the public is entitled to insist that the AEC be geared to the realities of today and not to the exploded premises of 1946.

The reality is that the Atom has not justified the separate and unique status which Congress understandably assigned it in 1946.

The Atom has *not* been the single necessary weapon.

The Atom has *not* revolutionized industrial society.

The Atom has *not* produced revolutionary advances in medicine or industry.

The peaceful Atom has *not* ushered in a "New World" but has rather become a *part*, quite a minor part, of the old one.

And yet the official sponsor and trustee of the Atom in this country, the Atomic Energy Commission, has hardly changed at all.

A revision of the AEC so that its functions conform to the facts of today would seem to be in order. To recommend the details of how such an up-dating ought to be worked out by transfer of functions and even loppings-off is certainly not a responsibility of mine or of any other private citizen. Whether the AEC should

117

have one administrator in place of its present five commissioners, or whether such-and-such a division ought to be reduced from fifty desks to one or two, these matters are of interest to me chiefly as a taxpayer.

What *does* concern me more is that steps are taken to get the Atom fully back into the stream of American life, and in a role of proper proportions. I want my government to continue to encourage through every means the broad growth of scientific research and development, and that means *all* of science; not, as in the past, singling out the Atom for preferential treatment. I do not want atomic science, because of the euphoria of the past or by present lobbying power, to secure more than its justifiable share of our research resources of trained brains and money. If the most efficient way of ensuring a balanced over-all scientific development for the nation means transferring some functions from the AEC and turning these over, say, to the more broadly based National Science Foundation, then I would be heartily in favor of such a move.

Similarly, I favor continuing technical and financial aid, on a selective basis, to underdeveloped countries, and if in certain instances such aid would be wisely supplemented by an atomic research or power installation, well and good. But the idea of a *separate* atomic Point IV Program, carried on almost as if the larger and more comprehensive scheme of foreign aid did not exist, makes no sense to me whatever.

For many of the same reasons that the Atom was put by law into a special and separate administrative body, the responsibilities of the Congress for the Atom's development, as a weapon and for peaceful uses, were also given to a special and separate Congressional Joint Committee on Atomic Energy. And as the AEC became deeply involved in military policy and in crucial areas of our foreign relations, so did the Joint Atomic Energy Committee of Congress.

Now if the Atom had proved to be the decisive and almost sole reliance of our military security, then this broad responsibility of the Joint Committee over the area of military affairs might be justified. But of course we now know this all-atomic doctrine no longer fits the facts. By the same token if today the Atom had proved itself to be all-pervasive in foreign relations then the broad and sometimes decisive influence of the Joint Atomic Committee in foreign relations might appropriately continue. But this is not the case. One could cite a long roster of American participation in economic and diplomatic issues all over the world in which the Atom plays no role at all, or a subordinate one; and yet the Joint Committee continues to exercise a powerful influence on the whole of our foreign relations and military affairs through its special responsibility for the Atom. A few illustrations may illuminate the point.

During the evening of July 14, 1949, President Truman met with the members of the Joint Committee on

Atomic Energy at Blair House. Others in attendance included the Secretary of State, Mr. Acheson; General Eisenhower, then President of Columbia University, one of the nation's great statesmen in the military field; the Secretary of Defense, Mr. Johnson; and the writer as Chairman of AEC. The President stated the position of his Administration that there be resumed that close cooperation and joint undertaking in the field of atomic weapons that existed when the United Kingdom had been a wartime partner of the United States in the scientific, technical, and manufacturing aspects of the first atomic bombs.

The position of the President involved a number of matters of great concern to our two nations and to the security of the Western world. The narrowest consideration was the economy of effort, greater technical effectiveness, and greater physical security that continuation of the wartime collaboration with the United Kingdom could provide. But far broader issues than these issues about nuclear weapons and their development were directly involved. This kind of partnership with the UK had far-reaching military implications; therefore General Eisenhower was asked to express his opinion, which was in support of the proposition. The position of the Administration also had numerous diplomatic implications of the most far-reaching nature.

Opposition within the Joint Atomic Committee to the President's proposal for resumption of cooperative

British and American relations defeated the Administration's position. The issue did not go to the Committee on Foreign Relations nor to the Committees on the Armed Forces but was decided, in practical effect, by a Committee whose jurisdiction was limited to the Atom.

The position of the President seemed to me, as Chairman of the AEC, a sound one. But it is not the *merits* of President Truman's position that I am examining here. My present point is that so portentous a question of foreign policy of the United States was dealt with decisively by a specialized Committee dealing with the Atom rather than by the Committee on Foreign Relations. The fact that on the Joint Committee were Senators who were also members of the Committee on Foreign Relations did not, I submit, change the basic point of the unsuitability of having a Joint Committee on the Atom having a decisive role in so critical an issue of our foreign policy. The rejection of the President's position was resented by the British Government—and with justification, I believe—as a repudiation of the close relationship that had existed during the war, a partnership which in every other area the United States as well as the United Kingdom wished to continue.

Another illustration of the powerful influence of the Joint Committee upon the whole spectrum of our foreign relations through its special jurisdiction over the Atom is a more recent one. The French Government not long ago requested technical information, and permission to purchase hardware items from American manufacturers, that would help them in developing their atomic program, including an atomic submarine. It has been generally reported that the President and his Administration were opposed to assisting the French Government in developing a separate atomic weapons and atomic energy program. To what extent that opposition stemmed from or was in anticipation of *legislative* resistance to the French request from the Joint Atomic Committee is a matter of conjecture; but it is relevant to the question I raise about the scope of legislative policy jurisdiction over foreign affairs of the Joint Committee that it was *that Committee* rather than the Committee on Foreign Relations that had primary responsibility for what may have been a key issue affecting our total relations with France.

It is not a remote possibility that the outcome might have been different, if the Foreign Relations Committee had handled this issue. The responsibility of this Committee is as broad as that of the Joint Atomic Committee is narrow; the application of this broad point of view to the French request might well have led to a different legislative position, which in turn might have influenced the Executive position.

In any event the resulting rejection of the French Government's requests offended the French. It affected the entire range of our diplomatic relations with the central nation of the Common Market and of NATO and the NATO military forces. It may well be that these episodes of rejection and noncooperation sparked President de Gaulle's estrangement from this country on issues of the Common Market and trade, and contributed decisively to his ultimate conclusion that France must create an atomic military posture independent of the United States and its atomic war-time partner, the United Kingdom.

Healthy working relations with the French Government are basic to the health of the whole of our relations with Europe and the United Kingdom. The French, with their mature atomic energy program, will soon build an atomic submarine anyway, but history may record that it was the refusal of the Joint Committee on Atomic Energy to exchange of atomic information with the French that ignited antagonism between the United States and France, with consequences that have affected the whole texture of world security and endangered, for a time, the unity of the alliances, military and economic, which are fundamental to our security.

These issues of security, diplomacy, and international trade policy have for generations been the primary legislative responsibility of the Committees of Congress on Foreign Relations and the Armed Services. The "liaison" (including cross-membership) by various means between the Joint Atomic Committee as a body and these appropriate Committees of foreign affairs and the military may be ever so good, but it is

123

the Joint Committee that is recognized in the Congressional fraternity as the "expert" on the Atom. The largely out-dated but still potent aura of secrecy about the Atom sustains the Joint Committee's position of exclusiveness and expertness in relation to other committees and other individual members of Congress.

Is this not again a case of artificially separating the Atom from the whole context of human affairs? This separation may have been valid in 1946, but it is questionable and probably damaging today. Can military and diplomatic affairs be thus artificially fragmented without injury to the unity of those policies and without hampering the conduct of defense and diplomacy by the Executive?

Or take yet another current illustration—also an important one—of the way in which the Joint Committee on the Atom has come to occupy a separate and unique role hard to justify by the facts of today.

In years of negotiation with the Soviet Union the issue of a ban on nuclear weapons testing has come to be treated as if it were basic to our foreign policy. The issues in such a negotiation are only partly technical and "atomic"; they are essentially political and must be made a part of the whole fabric of our foreign relations. A number of Senators not members of the Joint Committee have spoken out forcefully on this issue. Yet the primary *legislative* role, which of course includes not only systematic fact-finding but policy judgments, has thus far been in the hands of the Joint

Atomic Energy Committee, not the Senate Foreign Relations Committee. If such a treaty should at some time be agreed upon by the President and the Soviet Union, it must, under our Constitution, be with the "advice and consent" of the Senate, which in practice usually means the Senate Committee on Foreign Relations. Does this Joint Atomic Energy Committee's separateness further or hinder a unified approach to this problem? On this issue of atomic testing, heralded by some as the first step toward disarmament—a position I find unpersuasive—is it not true that the Joint Atomic Energy Committee, as a body of both houses, is impinging on grave responsibilities of the Senate, responsibilities which the Senate has assigned to its Foreign Relations Committee almost since the founding of the Republic? I find this disturbing because the purview of the Joint Committee as such is not broad enough to qualify it to act as a foreign relations committee.

This kind of constitutional and legislative confusion of function shows how far the artificial apartness of the Atom from the whole context of life has led us all astray.

The purpose of this chapter has been to question whether the structure erected in 1946, the AEC and the Joint Committee, can meet the needs of the present. I hope for vigorous public discussion and probing, not of the fitness of the individuals who make up these two bodies—this is not at issue—but of the sound-ness, the workability, and the results of the *structure* of these agencies. Are they adapted to their present task, or are they anachronisms?

Public discussion of this issue has been singularly lacking. This is partly because of the hang-over of a mystique of secrecy and a misplaced worship of the infallibility of scientists and experts. These have tended to inhibit the lay public and those members of Con-gress who are not on the Joint Committee from exam-ining these questions with the gloves-off vigor their importance to the country requires.

I detect a profound and significant change in rela-tions and functions *between* the Joint Committee and the AEC since the time I served on the Commission. The Joint Committee in its earlier years was the "watchdog," critical of AEC at every step, demanding results or detailed reasons why results were not forth-coming. The Joint Committee at that time followed the tradition of the Constitution: determining policy and securing an accounting of results were the legislative responsibilities of the Committee; execution was the sole responsibility of the AEC.

Somewhere along the line—I think I could bracket the time if it were relevant—the relationship of the Joint Committee to the AEC as to civilian atomic power was modified. It became less the watchdog and critic and more the advocate of the atomic power pro-gram, even to the point of deciding from time to time the kind of atomic reactors AEC was to build or subsidize.

This change raises another question about the effectiveness of the AEC-Joint Committee structure.

As protagonist of a large civilian atomic power program, the Joint Committee's function as watchdog and critic has been diverted, so far as a civilian power program is concerned, to a quite different function than that conceived by the Joint Committee at the time of the AEC on which I served. Not that the Joint Committee's investigative role at that time was a soothing and a pleasant one for those of us in the Commission; at times it was onerous and time-consuming; sometimes the inquiries seemed not only over-severe but irrelevant. But that critical function of the Committee was a necessary and a crucial one.

However, as the years went by the Committee has assumed increasingly not only the legislative policy role but part of the executive responsibility as well. This is usually expressed in the details of the language of the annual authorization legislation written by the Committee itself as a prelude to appropriations. No wonder then that the Committee has tended to become more a formulator and defender of the program than primarily a probing critic. Such a mixture of functions tends to make the Joint Committee more an apologist for the AEC than was the Committee in the earlier days when, not having a hand in program formulation but only in policy, it was freer critically to investigate how the AEC was discharging its executive responsibility. The wisdom of the Founding Fathers in separating policy and execution has rarely been better illustrated.

At the core of this issue of the functional suitability of the roles of the AEC and the Joint Committee is the concept of the Atom, vintage of 1946, as a mystical thing separate and apart from the mainstream of American life, to be dealt with by radical departures from our traditions of technical progress and of democratic processes by which the public interest has been protected and promoted.

Nothing better illustrates this thesis and points out the dangers in this doctrine than the final illustration to which I want to call attention: the protection of the public from the dangers to life and safety from the radiation produced by the splitting of the peaceful Atom, aptly described as "the most deadly, the most dangerous process that man has ever conceived."*

Two kinds of instances involving the public health and safety serve to illuminate the issue of *functional* fitness of the AEC and Joint Committee.

The first concerns so-called low-level radiation material, usually called radioactive isotopes, now produced in AEC installations and widely and beneficially used in industrial operations or research, and in hospitals. These are substances which must be

* Power Reactor Development Co. v. International Union 367 U.S. 396, dissenting opinion of Justices Douglas and Black, p. 410 (1961).

128

handled with care, for otherwise they can be injurious to human beings. The radioactive substances are put into specially designed containers and shipped from AEC production centers to the point of use, by public transport. After the low-level radioactive isotopes are "spent" and no longer useful in an industry or hospital they still are not safe and must somehow be disposed of. The AEC recently reported that there have been 47 "accidents" in such shipments; in 18 cases small quantities were spilled and in 15 cases there were "severe impact accidents."

A few years ago, quite by chance, the public discovered that containers of such radioactive waste products were being dumped into the coastal waters of Massachusetts. In that area fishing is an important industry and a source of food for the whole northeast. In the summer the beaches are used by hundreds of thousands of people for recreation. This dumping was done with the permission of the AEC, but apparently the approval or advice of the marine biologists at Woods Hole and the state and federal agencies having responsibility for health was not obtained or sought by AEC. There was a wave of public denunciation of this seemingly casual AEC way of dealing with potential hazards to the health of many people.

The AEC suffered in prestige by this unfortunate assumption that, because radiation was its field, it was also expert on public health.

A far more serious consequence: by this sense of

atomic apartness the state and federal public health services were *deprived of the opportunity* to become fully knowledgeable of the radiation hazards in such wastes and how to protect against them. Now, happily, bit by bit functions of AEC that involve existing federal or state technical agencies are being transferred to those nonatomic agencies. This is a move in the direction I urge: putting the Atom into the mainstream of men's affairs, not artificially keeping it separate and apart.

Getting rid of low-level radioactive wastes of this kind is bad enough if dealt with as it was in the case of Cape Cod. The risk of damage in the Cape Cod case or of the 47 reported "accidents" in shipments, as far as we now know, is relatively limited and may not therefore be a matter of grave concern. But a whole series of atomic power plants located within or near populated centers has recently been vigorously recommended by the AEC, by the Joint Committee, by the principal manufacturers of atomic power plants, and by some leading electrical utilities, private and publicly owned. The utility supplying New York City, for example, is strongly pressing its plans for the largest atomic power plant in the country, to be located within the heart of the city, adjacent to a population of several million people.

Such a program as the AEC and others project presents a waste disposal problem of such proportions that it must be taken with the utmost seriousness. We are told that in another fifteen years or less a substantial percentage of the electricity of the country will be produced in atomic power plants. Dr. Donald R. Chadwick, Chief of the Division of Radiological Health of the US Public Health Service, estimated, in April 1963, that "the accumulated volume of radioactive wastes from nuclear installations . . . will increase from about one and a half million gallons, the estimated 1965 volume, to two billion gallons in 1995." These huge quantities of radioactive wastes *must somehow be removed* from the reactors, must, without mishap, be put into containers that will never rupture; then these vast quantities of poisonous stuff must be moved either to a burial ground or to reprocessing and concentration plants, handled again, and disposed of, by burial or otherwise, *with a risk of human error at every step*. Two billion gallons of waste in 1995 leads Dr. Chadwick to comment: "It is in the development of atomic energy, however, where lies our greatest potential [environmental] contamination problem if uncontrolled."

Precisely here, in overcoming these risks, is potentially the most catastrophic and worrisome consequences of what is happening to the public policy concepts of the agencies that are entrusted with the Atom— the AEC and the Joint Committee. Surely it is prudent that *before* a program of building these "large" plants in or near populated areas over the country goes farther, this problem must be realistically and fearlessly and above all candidly confronted and conquered by the AEC, the Joint Committee, and the manufacturers of atomic power plants who have put so much of their stockholders' money into this supposedly profitable prospect.

To project as a goal of our government, as the AEC does, a program for the construction of "ten to twelve full-scale [large] power plants during the next dozen years" *until* a safe method to meet this problem of waste disposal has been *demonstrated* seems to me irresponsible in dealing with public and private funds; more important, it reveals a disturbing attitude about the importance of protecting public health and safety against catastrophic mistakes that might occur.

A layman need not be familiar with the technical engineering details of a particular atomic power plant design to comprehend the nature of this danger in the disposition of radioactive wastes and the potential consequences of proceeding with a widespread national atomic power program until assurance is doubly sure about safety as *demonstrated over a period of time in a full-scale plant operation.*

The basic facts are simple: you cannot have an atomic power plant unless you produce large quantities of radiation. The atomic "fuel" for this radiation peters out and must be replaced, from time to time. When the fuel elements are removed, they are still radioactive. Radioactivity remains in that removed waste product, and there is no magic that can make it simply disappear. These highly poisonous wastes must then be handled for their removal, must be transported in some kind of containers and vehicles from the power plant itself to some place far removed from populated areas, there to be processed in a plant (such as one now being built in upper New York state) and then ultimately buried, still radioactive, in an atomic grave-yard.

At a cost that the AEC states is not yet known, the risks of this handling can be reduced, and the experts say now, as they told me as AEC Chairman fifteen years ago, that there is nothing to worry about, that engineering can take care of all of this and the layman need not worry his poor nontechnical brain about it. The layman and the public official quite properly may have 100 percent confidence in the integrity *but not in the infallibility* of those who give him these assurances. For a new technical venture the safety record has been very good indeed. But there have been "accidents," some serious; there can be others. One such major accident, one serious miscalculation in an atomic power plant in this early stage of development, one failure of a container in the heart of a populated area could be a disaster. Insurance companies have refused to provide complete coverage against such an even-tuality, which could involve millions of people and billions of dollars of property loss or damage. More-over the intelligent layman senses, I think, that if there is any chance of such disaster, that is too much of a chance to take for electricity that is the same as the kind he now uses and at the same or greater cost to him.

What public policy demands or justifies going ahead with a program in which there are still these unresolved risks to human health and safety? The answer is not that the national security requires taking such risks, as may be in the case of the testing of atomic weapons in the atmosphere, nor because there are not other equally cheap ways of producing the same kind of electricity. In the production of no other source of electrical energy, whether by oil, gas, coal, or water power, is there ever a remotely comparable serious consequence of human failure, whether of design, material, equipment, or operation. Then just why are we urged to plunge ahead with this program of large reactors especially in or adjacent to heavily populated areas? Laymen are entitled to know the answer, not in technical terms but in terms of public policy.

There is one proposition that a layman can understand, perhaps better than most experts seem to: however many gadgets are involved, *human beings* are in charge of atomic power plants; human beings design the safety measures, build the containers, operate the equipment by which these materials are transported and buried in the earth. When the President of the Consolidated Edison Company of New York, commenting on an atomic power plant his company proposes to build in the heart of New York City, told the annual meeting of his stockholders in the spring of

134

1963 that he was convinced that a power plant of this design (and presumably the disposition of its poisonous wastes) is "absolutely safe," he was saying in effect that the phenomenon of human error had been repealed.

What concerns me here is not that men engage in such wishful thinking about the possibilities of human error where the consequences could be disastrous to so many people, or even to a very few. It is that the public bodies which should be the advocates and guardians of our safety have tended more and more to become the proponents of a national atomic power program *before a method to eliminate these hazards has been fully demonstrated.*

When I was Chairman of the AEC, from 1946 to 1950, highly poisonous radioactive wastes were being produced at all the AEC reactors. The largest quantities were at the weapons material establishment at Hanford, Washington, selected because it was a remote site. When the radioactive elements in the reactor, similar in essentials to those in an atomic power plant, had to be replaced they were gingerly removed by remote control gadgets, put into heavy containers, and buried near Hanford. Substantially the same procedure is followed today; the graveyard is now a very large one indeed, after all these years, and represents a huge public expense.

The risks of such a crude method of dealing with these poisons can be amply justified where the output

135

of a plant is for weapons for our defense, as was and is the case at Hanford, and where the burial ground and the plant are located close together, far from densely populated centers. But surely something better must be devised and demonstrated to be workable where (1) the national defense is not involved, (2) the atomic power plant merely produces the same kind of electricity that a risk-free "conventional" power plant produces, and (3) the location is near or in the heart of a populated center such as New York City.

During the years that intervened between the first AEC and the present time has the problem of disposition of these poisonous wastes been made demonstrably manageable, either as to danger or cost?

The answer is No. When in February 1963 in the Stafford Little Lectures at Princeton I made incidental reference to the hazards in a large-scale civilian atomic power program, the Joint Committee invited me to appear before it. I was reminded that the Committee had not overlooked the problem, that it had been following it assiduously, that much money had been spent on the problem. The following day a member of the AEC was called as a witness; he referred to the money expended on the problem and indicated that there was nothing to fear, really, although no method had been demonstrated, even in a pilot plant; a solution was just a matter of cost, as yet uncertain.

I find something disturbing in this episode, and it is relevant to this analysis of the structure of the relationship that has developed between the AEC and the Joint Committee. No questions of a remotely critical or probing kind were put to the Commissioner by the Joint Committee on his testimony, nor on the AEC's Report, just made to the President, that methods for safe handling of waste poisons, though stated to be of very great importance, after all these years and all the money expended, *are still in the research stage*; that there has not yet been a pilot plant demonstration; that there has yet to be even a field experiment.*

Should not a program of large-scale atomic reactors wait at least until it is demonstrated that this waste poison problem is decisively "licked"? So long as the safe handling of radioactive wastes for a large-scale national atomic power program is still in the research stage, as the AEC Report to the President states, *the future of atomic energy as a major reliance for civilian electricity is in grave doubt.* These risks may limit or even eliminate a nation-wide atomic energy program.

The AEC is not only the over-all protagonist of a nation-wide atomic power program; it is also the body which must sit as judge of the safety to the public of the design, mode of construction, and site of particular atomic power plants. In short the AEC as a general promoter of atomic power must also decide the quasi-judicial issue of whether a license is issued. With a world of good will and integrity and technical com-

* Pages 54 and 55 of the AEC's Report to the President on "Civilian Nuclear Power" dated November 20, 1962.

petence on the part of the AEC, how well is the public protected by this dual and conflicting role?

The shakiness of this advocate or promoter-judge role is compounded when the Joint Committee's eagerness to press a nation-wide atomic power plant program is added to the balance of considerations. Add too the fact that manufacturers of this equipment are naturally pressing, in good faith, to sell their products on a large scale. Add too the fact that to a large extent outside experts on safety of site and design in local health departments, or consultants, are almost of necessity alumni of the AEC staff or of the manufacturers' organizations.

These considerations emphasize how sobering it is that the members of the Joint Committee—certainly those who are most active—as to civilian atomic power have become less critical and probing, more advocates, than in the days when the AEC and the Joint Committee maintained a definitely arms-length relationship.

The change in the AEC-Joint Committee relationship, if my observation of the change is a correct one, is not something new and strange in the relations of certain Executive agencies and Committees of Congress, however contrary it is to what years ago I asserted to be my conception of the correct division of functions between the Legislative and the Executive. What makes this a saddening development, as I see it, is that it is a symptom of an unhappy down-grading of a great scientific discovery to "just another government activity" run by "just another" bureaucracy—and bureaucracy I define as any public organization primarily concerned with what happens *to it*.

"The New Atomic World" seems to be deteriorating so far that unless there is a turn in direction it will become just part of the bureaucratic scramble for Congressional patrons, no less inspiring, but no more so, than any one of the tired and middle-aged bureaus of government.

It seems to me therefore that however irritating the question may be to my friends and former colleagues in the AEC and to its industrial and scientific contractors, and perhaps to some members of the Joint Committee on Atomic Energy, the question should be raised and discussed: Is the AEC-Joint Committee plan the best way—or is there a better way—to protect and promote the public interest in the peaceful Atom? Can the original watchdog role of the Joint Committee be restored—or should the whole idea of whether there should be a Joint Committee, in view of the changed circumstances since 1946, be debated candidly and re-examined? As a private citizen I hope that what I have written here will serve to encourage just such a re-examination.

CHAPTER VIII

———————•○•———————

CHANGE AND HOPE

ONE HAS ONLY to look at the first page of our daily newspapers on almost any day to see how deep is our leadership's constant preoccupation with nuclear weapons as an essential to our security and the road to peace.

One day it is a ban on testing of nuclear weapons that occupies the front page; we are told that without a ban the genie is hopelessly out of the bottle or that the fall-out will be disastrous; or contrariwise, that without testing of these weapons our own security is in danger. The next day it is perhaps a nuclear missile-equipped submarine fleet or surface vessels in place of land bases that is our urgent security need and Answer. The next day it may be a proposal for a multi-national NATO nuclear agreement sharing responsibility for nuclear weapons, and the next day the Senate floor rings with talk of a new kind of bomb, a Neutron bomb, or other kinds of additions to our nuclear armament. Or, at the other end of the spectrum of proposals that fill the pages and airwaves are those for means of slowing up the "proliferation" of nuclear arms by somehow preventing France or China from becoming nuclear powers, or some basis for agreeing with the unwilling Russians on some limitation on nuclear armament.

Anything about nuclear weapons commands attention. The amount of emotional energy and time almost any statement or proposal about nuclear arms, however remote from reality, receives from our leadership and from conscientious citizens compared with any of the many other more prosaic but attainable short steps towards peace is testimony to the bewitchment and the fear that has fallen over us about the Atom. Stupendous are the number of words that have piled up about atomic weapons every year since Hiroshima, in speeches, pronouncements from the Kremlin or the Geneva conferences or conclaves of scientists or ban-the-bomb demonstrations in Trafalgar Square; this is one measure of the world's preoccupation with this single subject.

None of this succession of proposals, and little of the rhetoric or the demonstrations or the petitions or the picketing or the messages of the President or of Chairman Khrushchev or the editorial writers gives one a sense of hope.

And yet there is hope. As time goes on, in my opinion, that hope becomes more sturdy.

Early in this book, beginning with a personal foreword and continuing through much of what I have written, I have said there is hope but that we will not find it by threshing and re-threshing this old straw of ideas about what to do now about nuclear weapons.

141

This concluding chapter suggests where I think our hope lies. It lies, in my opinion, in the vivid life-giving imagination-stirring waves of change upon change that are the chief characteristic of our times. This line of thought I can introduce best by reciting a personal experience in 1949 when I was still Chairman of the Atomic Energy Commission.

My wife and I were on vacation on the island of Martha's Vineyard off Cape Cod. On the evening of September 19th we had gone into town for dinner with friends, and by eleven o'clock, when we started back, a fog had settled down so heavily that we could hardly see our way on the little road that led to the old house we had rented.

In my personal journal for that day, my notes read as follows:

"The headlights picked out the figure of a man, hatless, squinting into the lights, looking bemused, hooking his thumb in the hitch-hiker's gesture (though of course there's nothing beyond to hitch to but the gate). I said quietly: 'It's Jim McCormack' [Brigadier General James McCormack, Director of the Division of Military Applications of the U.S. Atomic Energy Commission], as if I frequently found him on a wind-swept moor, in the dead of night, on an island, outside a goat field.

" 'I have a message for you,' he said, and we drove down to the house in silence. There I lighted a kerosene lamp, and he and I went to the upstairs sitting room."

The young General said ruefully that Roman messengers who brought evil tidings were given a rough time, so he was ready for anything. He then went on to deliver his unhappy message.

The Air Force, in cooperation with the AEC, had been conducting round-the-clock flights in planes equipped with air filters, a procedure first proposed by President Conant of Harvard and Vannevar Bush of MIT to detect whether the Russians had set off an atomic explosion. Analysis of such a filter established that they had. The United States A-bomb monopoly had come to an end.

This was the message General McCormack had brought me; by shortly after dawn we were on our way back to Washington, where other men in government were learning the bitter news.

In my journal for November 1, 1949, I find an entry that reflects the effect of this news on some of those in the circle of policy makers at that time:

"Last evening a couple of hours in my office with Senator McMahon. Pretty discouraging. What he is talking is the inevitability of war with the Russians, and what he says adds up to one thing: blow them off the face of the earth, quick, before they do the same to us—and we haven't much time. He uses all sorts of words to justify this, and part of the time he is practicing speeches on the floor of the Senate at us.

143

The whole world revolves about the exploding Atom, as he sees it—that's the whole of it, and there is no hope.

"I said, 'I don't believe that.' Apparently one isn't supposed to say that, for he didn't like it. I was asked for 'evidence' to support my belief that things aren't as cut and dried and desperate as he painted them."

In this troubled period all manner of proposals were debated within our government. One of these, the result of a preoccupation with the Bomb, was indeed preventive war. This was not an impulsive reaction of one Senator alone, not by any means. The solution of "drop the A-bomb and have it over with" had not a little public verbal support.

During those days of anxiety a wise man made this comment on the preoccupation with a one-shot "solution" to our fears, "drop the Bomb." He said to me: "If we do that—just leave aside the terrible ethical stain this would be on the American people—if we do that, we make it impossible that there shall *ever* be a change in what today looks so hopeless. My advice," he continued, "is this: Don't prevent change from having a chance. On the contrary, give change a chance: more than that, help it along."

Give change a chance: this injunction was a wise one then and still is, for it recognizes a towering fact of importance far greater than the mounting arsenals of atomic weapons; that fact is that by taking advantage of change men can manage to avert dangers and build a future.

The world we live in is indeed a world of change, and change is the condition of human existence.

How many men could have fairly estimated in 1945, even by an order of magnitude, the change that produced the tornado of national anger and resentment that now shakes the continent of Africa?

Today, who can venture to say what social transformation will result from perhaps the greatest of all human migrations, the march from the land to the cities that is now taking place, particularly in the underdeveloped nations?

Who is there that foresaw clearly that the boon of medical progress would in a generation so greatly increase population as to upset the economies and social structures of many countries; who can now foretell what the world-wide movement for population control, if successful, may bring in its wake, by way of social, political, and religious consequences of the most far-reaching kind?

Who could have foreseen even a few years ago so vast a change that we must consider whether Communist China may not become, may now be indeed, more of a threat to Communist Russia than the Capitalist West; or that France and West Germany would no longer be hostile?

Who could foresee changes that made racial peace the most critical problem of America in 1963?

Who could have foreseen that a letter to President Roosevelt from a kindly professor in Princeton, Albert Einstein, would result in a change in the whole of military and diplomatic concepts; or that the rise of a flamboyant commando in the little island of Cuba could for weeks put the whole world on the brink of a holocaust?

The currents of change run for the most part in deep tidal movements far below the surface. There even the most perceptive eye cannot detect their beginnings. They are not predictable and in their embryo state not even detectable; all we know is that changes are under way. Therefore, to cite specific cases of the kind of change I have in mind almost obscures the essential point of their unpredictability and wide diversity. Nevertheless, a few references to changes that serve the cause of peace may help us to be sensitive to, to recognize, and to encourage the beginnings of changes that, in my view, bear mightily on the central problem of maintaining peace in the world and ultimately bringing to an end the nightmare of overhanging nuclear war.

Without a sense of where our hope lies, we shall continue our fear-ridden preoccupation with peace through weapons; or negotiating for the destruction of weapons by agreement, we may continue to be transfixed by the hopeless dilemma of two antagonists armed so that they can destroy each other and the world. Such a fixation, unmitigated, will in time crush

146

hope and creativity and slow up the change out of which good things can come.

For it is the essence of my point of hope that a continued concentration upon eliminating nuclear weapons makes the affirmative though less dramatic changes less fruitful, because we will underrate their value and divert and distract emotional energy from those non-military areas where our best hope lies.

So as I draw toward the close of these discussions of the Atom, I offer one man's faith that *a world of change is a world of hope*.

My faith that we shall avoid the disaster that threatens is a personal belief, not capable of explicit or logical demonstration or proof. It is a faith in the potentialities that lie in changes, in thousands of kinds of changes that are making more and more men and women, statesmen and private individuals alike, sense a human drawing together, a slow but steady increase in an awareness of the reality of our human interdependence, on a thousand fronts, the often prosaic but objective evidences of our common heritage, our growing bonds of mutual need, the "common moorings" that bind men to men and peoples to peoples.

I shall later refer to a few instances of the kind of changes toward peace. But I remind myself that, from my observation and participation in the changes that are under way among ordinary peoples of the world, many, perhaps most of the changes are not now recognizable; they are deep within the minds and emotions

147

of men. But the seeds of daring change have been planted and, often in unseen places, are germinating.

Our world simply will not sit still to be fitted for all-embracing theories. To me, therefore, the world of those who prophesy doom or the millennium is not a real world. In the changing world that I know, there are always reasons for deep anxiety—and there are always reasons, too, for hope.

A narrow preoccupation with the Bomb is myopic because it fails to see the potential heights of human achievement, and part of my own sense of hope is based on what I have seen men accomplish. I have seen men achieve the *possible*. I have seen them coping with—not solving, but learning to deal with, to manage—the intricate, contradictory, and refractory problems bound up in their lives as members of a community or a state or a nation or a group of nations. Never have I seen them utterly solve human problems. A basic thesis of this book is that human problems— the great questions of war and peace and also the little questions of family harmony and neighborhood relations—are not susceptible of solution in the sense that scientific questions are solved. Man is too complex, too various, too wonderfully changeable for that.

The concept of Solution is the concept of perfection. It does have a role in the world. From it have sprung the greatest and noblest moral insights and religious ideals. It is certainly not my purpose to deprecate the aspirations which raise up the souls of men.

But by itself, the concept of Solution is an imperfect, even a dangerous, guide. Man is glorious not only because he is capable of formulating great goals, but because he is also capable of moving, achievement by achievement, in their direction. In our country, we have never finally "solved" any basic question. We have never quite lived up to the idealism that animates our Constitution. But being a practical and imaginative people, not easily disheartened by setbacks and disappointments, we have managed, we have coped with our problems successfully enough so that we have not been crushed by poverty, or torn irreconcilably apart by civil disorder, or stagnated by social tensions.

We have not solved, but managed. As a guide to the way in which human affairs are conducted, how achievement actually happens, I would like to suggest that we think in terms not of Solution but of manageable possibilities.

In a world of change where men are acting to achieve the possible, I do see hope. Not one gigantic hope of ultimate Solution, but a thousand hopes of building, stone by stone, an edifice of the do-able; this rising structure makes possible the next step and then the next, so that what was once seemingly impossible becomes ever closer to realization.

In the hammering out of changes toward peace, wrought by this process of the manageable job, negotiated armament agreements between the powers will be only an incident or consequence, not a cause. These changes instead will lie in that complex spectrum outside the area of armament, changes that govern the course of mankind because they spring from man's everyday needs, his commonplace desires, and are within his considerable but finite capacities.

Here is one example that illustrates how exceptional men, by a patient attention to the art of achieving the possible, have brought within reach and have grasped what would otherwise have been impossible.

In June 1950 I visited the then head of Economic Planning in France, M. Jean Monnet, at his thatched country house near Paris. His gardener, he said, a solid kind of man and a veteran of the last war, had told him: "Monsieur Monnet, we must get along with the Germans. We, the French and the Germans, can't go on fighting." "Now," said Monnet, "that is a revolutionary thought in France, but my gardener is right. What he said is really the simple idea behind what we're trying to do in bringing about economic unity in Europe, what we call the Schuman Plan."

A few days later I visited with the British Prime Minister, Clement Attlee and heard a debate in the Commons on whether the United Kingdom should accept France's invitation to join the Schuman Plan. Attlee, then leader of the Labor Party, is a long-headed sophisticated statesman, but both he and the then leader of the Conservative opposition, Winston Churchill, thought the Schuman Plan had no future and certainly that the great British Commonwealth should not accept the urgent invitation to join a supra-national European enterprise. Which it didn't.

All this was in 1950. What Monnet and his gardener and the public authorities that represent them have done is now widely known as an accomplished fact: The Common Market. Now the United Kingdom's admission to this supra-national enterprise—as I write still in doubt—will be on less favorable terms.

Europe in 1963 is a changed dominion. It is fast becoming a powerful economic, and more and more a political, unity. What the diplomacy of Metternich could not accomplish, what the military genius of Napoleon and the blood of French soldiers could not accomplish, is now a fact of towering import in this fluid creative world of today. No one with a slide rule or a lot of statistics could have predicted this. It grew out of the unpredictable emotions and drive of people. In that strange way of human affairs in which unpredictable consequences become more important than the predictable ones, the burgeoning political unity of Europe that grew out of or was made possible by the Marshall Plan and the Schuman Plan dealt not directly with peace at all but with economic development.

Enmity and distrust still exist among the Western European nations. These antagonisms have not been "solved." But the program that has grown out of the Marshall Plan and the Coal and Steel Authority has created a structure within which the containment of these enmities has become progressively more possible. France and Germany and the other nations of the Common Market are now bound together in many important ways. Their prosperity and interdependence have given them an enormous stake in peace; and therefore the chance of losing this stake through some nationalistic conflict has diminished.

In Western Europe a change quite unpredictable has already come about. There may be another, no less remarkable, in the making in Asia: the development of stable, peaceful cooperative relations between India and Pakistan.

Following the partition of the Indian subcontinent there was bloodshed and hatred between India and Pakistan, deep hostilities aggravated religious differences between two new nations burdened by overwhelming poverty. One issue seemed above others impossible of settlement: to whom does Kashmir belong, India or Pakistan? The question seems impossible of resolution—now. Yet within recent years, both nations have been cautiously working together in a quite different area, where a specific finite achievement beneficial and essential to both is possible: the equitable sharing and joint use of a great common resource, the waters of the Indus River basin, that have their headwaters largely in India and Kashmir, but which flow through West Pakistan and are her and India's great daily need for food production.

If this joint program continues to build on its formidable beginning—a treaty, and engineering works in progress—the result will be not merely to permit each nation to produce more food, but also to give India and Pakistan a larger stake in peaceful relations, a positive reason for peace, one that could lead to other agreements of common benefit. Kashmir is still a prickly issue, but already it is less central and immediate. With each additional step in economic cooperation, this political issue may well become less and less emotionally heated.

Kashmir may never be "solved." Opposing troops of India and Pakistan may remain face to face there for a generation. And yet the threat of war from this source could gradually be counterbalanced and then outweighed by the benefits of interdependence in other areas of common interest, so that it is conceivable that a formal disposition of the Kashmir question might become a matter almost of secondary importance.

But what has the European Common Market or Kashmir to do with saving the world from the Bomb?

A partial answer is that what has happened in Europe and may well be beginning in Asia *is* relevant to the Bomb. These examples of economic approaches to peace contain a lesson that is not remote at all.

Two world wars in this century have grown out of the bitter antagonism between Germany and France. Today as part of an economic rather than diplomatic effort only a decade old, western Europe is closer to economic unity than at any other time in history.

153

As a by-product of this economic union, steps have been taken toward political unity, something once considered quite impossible. But the most relevant aspect of this major event is that so long as these elements of unity of western Europe continue, this consequence ensues: that the bitter enemies, France and Germany, have effectively disarmed themselves.

France is not literally disarmed in the sense that she does not have weapons; West Germany is not disarmed in the sense that she has signed a treaty of disarmament with France. These countries are disarmed in an even deeper sense. They are disarmed because they have found that their common interests in leading the development of the community of Europe make any question of a disarmament treaty almost irrelevant.

If I am right that this is a form of true disarmament, then this point is worth reiterating: that disarmament between violently antagonistic countries, Germany and France, came about not through a preoccupation with armament but in a wholly different area, the area of trade and commerce, of cooperative economic development. The bonds of common interest that now link Germany and France, their stake in peace, are now so great that war between them seems not much more likely than war between such close friends as the United States and Canada.

True disarmament is not achieved by an oversimplified concentration on the elimination or the "balancing" of weapons. It comes about, I believe, from the

154

persistent, difficult, but *possible* series of actions that lessen the likelihood that war will take place by lessening some of the *causes* of war.

But how does the example of Europe possibly apply to the central source of fear today, the Communist superstates of Russia and China? We Americans have had and can continue to have a beneficial influence on the development of European unity; and we can help, too, in the growth of harmony between India and Pakistan, with whom we have good relations. But what bearing do these good and hopeful opportunities have on the question of war or peace with the Communist world?

Clearly, this is a wholly different matter. It is obviously not now possible for the United States or the West as a bloc to act toward Russia and Red China as we act among ourselves, in developing common concerns and multiplying the strands of interdependence. But this does not mean that the forces of change, change for the good, are not already at work within the Communist world, nor does it mean that the present state of hostility will remain forever fixed.

The hostility is deep and no man can predict how or whether it will ever abate, but there is at least one powerful force of change working toward a lessening hostility. This change is the rising prosperity of the Soviet Union. At times some of us have a tendency to be heartened by Russian difficulties at home—their agricultural failures, for example—as a piece of luck "for our side." But if we believe change that furthers stability with freedom works for peace, then the success of the Russian people in growing food, in building houses, and in continuing to raise their standard of living may be in our interest, in the whole world's interest. We might well be concerned about the Russian moon project not because they may be the first to reach the moon, but that such huge costly ventures are a serious distraction from something infinitely more important to the peace of the world, the building of a prosperous and therefore more conservative and less aggressive Russian society, one that in time may develop a desire for peace in place of their historic policy of fomenting instability and aggression everywhere.

An affluent Soviet state, whose citizens are enjoying the kind of consumer goods they want, at prices they can afford, taking vacations, owning cars and houses, and having the leisure to interest themselves in travel and the arts may be long in coming, but it is a change that appears to be on the way. What, I suggest, should trouble us more than an affluent Russia is one that is hungry, unsettled by internal tensions, lacking confidence in its future, a Russia that has little to lose and whose leaders seek foreign adventures to distract their own people's attention from their deprivations.

In the Communist world, Russia is relatively prosperous now; it is certainly not a have-not nation. Observers insist that it is a different Russia from the tense, jumpy, psychopathic days of Stalin. Poland is changing, too; and so even is Hungary, just a few years after the bloody repression of the revolution. The myth of the monolithic Communist world is breaking up under some of the same forces of change that are transforming societies throughout the globe.

We now see, for example, the spectacle of the once wild and woolly Bolsheviks of the Soviet Union presenting themselves, perhaps accurately, as a moderating force upon the maverick Red Chinese. Such are among the unpredictable turns and twists of events. More lie just ahead.

Perhaps the most important effect of Russia's economic success is not that it may be turning the aging fire-eating Bolsheviks into conventional, almost conservative, politicians; it is rather that the changes in Russia toward middle class prosperity may in a decade influence the now hell-and-high-water Chinese.

Visiting Chinese delegations see the Sputniks and the missiles, it is true; but they also see the cars, the well-stocked stores, the tractor plants, and the housing developments.

The progress of Russia *at home* in showing the Chinese what can be achieved for people's everyday physical well-being (freedom is another and more difficult kind of progress, God knows) may in time prove more consequential for peace than all the technical and economic aid the Russians have in the past provided directly to China. The Chinese are proud and independent; they are feeling their national strength as a world power for the first time. They are bitter and scornful toward what we in the West have achieved. But explaining Russia away to their own people is a more difficult matter.

While it is true that at this moment in history direct cooperative relations between the West and Russia and certainly China are severely limited and must be explored with caution, this by no means proves that the forces that move in the direction of stability and hope are entirely absent.

What can we do, as Americans, to take advantage of the hopeful and constructive kinds of change in the world? What can we do to "help change along," to multiply the bonds of interdependence among nations so that the reasons for peace outweigh the reasons for war?

There are many things that we are doing and can do. They may seem relatively unimportant now, compared to wiping out the overhanging threat of the Bomb, but if our point of view is broadened these activities will be seen as of real importance, more relevant to peace than any attempt to deal directly with weaponry or with the antagonistic Communist powers.

International commerce has always been a crucial factor in the political affairs of men. It has led to national rivalries and to wars, and, in other circumstances it has led to sustained peaceful relations. In our time we have witnessed some remarkable developments in this area. The European Common Market is of course the most striking, but there are others coming along that may be equally important. The multinational private corporation is one. There are now many private concerns, large and small, which not only operate in several countries or continents but which also have an international personnel—and even an international management and stock ownership. The development of these multinational enterprises is based on the hard practicality of businessmen. There is nothing of the "experiment in international living" about it. And yet the *effects*, in terms of helping create meaningful and durable bonds of common interest among peoples, could prove as effective as *direct* attempts through governments to draw men and nations together.

The international joint venture is another increasingly important aspect of international business life. Here two or more companies, from different countries, come together for some specific object—a small and indirect step toward peace but a real one.

Barter is becoming increasingly a useful tool for international trade, particularly where the barter is multinational. For one example, our plaguing mountains of surplus wheat and corn can be the foundation of *extensive* barter arrangements. To make this ancient and honorable device of barter effective on a really substantial scale some kind of International Trading Corporation may be needed; but the effect, whatever the mechanisms, is toward internationalizing trade, an undramatic factor toward peace but a real one.

There are, of course, many other areas where positive contributions toward peace are being made, and where much more can and ought to be done. The list of areas of opportunity is, happily, a long one, although for the purposes of this book I can do no more than mention several: international health and food programs; international science; education; the economic development of the underdeveloped nations; international developments of unity among religious groups once disunited or bitterly antagonistic.

These international forces of change are important, but even more crucial is the *source* of these changes. Here, I think, my discussion of the potentially hopeful aspects of the Soviet Union's economic progress is relevant. I have maintained that the strength of Russia as a stabilizing and cautionary influence in the Communist part of the world is directly bound up with the success of Russia in managing to meet the *demands of its own people* for their everyday needs.

So it is with us here, in America.

We think of the United States as the leader of the free world. We think of ourselves as the chief guardian and exponent of the values of the kind of civilization which has been developed in the West, and as the nation with the greatest responsibility to assist in the development of other friendly countries. And so we are.

But in the process of our dramatic emergence from isolation since 1940 we have tended to forget that this leadership is founded on what we have and can accomplish *here*, in our own country.

America does have responsibility of leadership in the world, and shoulders that responsibility nobly. In a masterful and mature way under President Kennedy, I think, and his predecessors, Presidents Eisenhower, Truman, and Roosevelt, our government has demonstrated our concern for the whole world, with full support of the American people. America has become indeed the trustee of some great basic principles of freedom.

But this world outlook must not be carried to an extreme that is self-defeating. It is not only charity that begins at home; strength also begins at home, and humaneness, and furthering and *demonstrating at home* the workability of these multiple roads toward peace in the world.

The security not alone of the United States but, to a degree not fully realized, mankind's hopes for peace, depend upon how well we demonstrate to other nations that the physical, cultural, and spiritual foundations of this Republic are steadily being strengthened and developed. The future of people everywhere depends upon how well we show that the concept of a civilized people in one great area of the world, the United States of America, has not been diluted or eroded by either an over-draft on our emotional energies for the noble goal of the well-being of other parts of the world, or as a subconscious escape from the problems at our own doorstep. We must not succumb to the human temptation to turn away from the things we can *do*, and can face up to, that are close to us—in our neighborhood, our home community, or in our country. And one of the most common ways of escaping those close-to-home needs and opportunities to act is to look across the seas or into space for our emotional satisfactions, or as a satisfying distraction from the more prosaic needs at home.

We are proud of the record of participation by this country in world affairs—in the military area, in diplomacy, in education, in human concern for other people, in music and in the arts, in every area, since the end of World War II. It is a record that is matchless in the history of humanism, of idealism, and of hard practical sense about the world.

But our concern for others outside America should not cause us to overlook a basic truth, basic to our efforts along the multiple roads toward a peaceful world: The hopes of the world for the protection and the continuation of human culture, in short, of a civilized world, will be determined by what happens in our own country. The demonstration of what it means to be free and productive and tolerant of each other, of what equality of opportunity for *every* human being

162

can mean, *will take place here in America if it takes place at all.*

We in America have many unsolved problems of our own. We are behind the goals we have set for ourselves, the potentials of our own development throughout the cities, towns, and countryside. In many ways we too are still an underdeveloped country, measured by our potentials and our goals.

I think most of us would put the education of our young people and the continued education of adults high on this list of things not to be neglected because of a concern for things farther away, whether it is on the moon or in India. Yet here in our own country, one that is founded on the idea of education, our teachers are too poorly trained, poorly paid, our schools and colleges and universities are too crowded, the curriculum and system of education in schools and colleges and universities quite out of phase with the utterly new problems young people must face. Our sense of responsibility for education the world over needs to be tempered by a realization of the needs here at home which are so urgent and unfulfilled.

Then there is another field, that of growing urbanization. In the past ten years or so, millions of people have left the small towns and farming areas of America to become part of cities or their immediate suburbs. This has had profound consequences on every institution, both in the countryside from which people have migrated, and in the cities and in the access to

163

cities. The comfort of living, the problems of recreation and of taxation, of housing, of water supply, of the purity of the air we breathe—can there be more challenging issues than these in Pakistan or Uganda, granting, as we do, that we are also deeply and sincerely concerned about those and all the other countries who are struggling with the problems of development?

Then there are whole regions of America the potentials of which are neglected. National attention to these, in a pioneering spirit, could greatly strengthen the whole of the United States. Here the analogy of the Valley of the Tennessee and the TVA comes to mind. Making the Tennessee Valley better for the people who live there has strengthened the whole of the United States. And so it would be if we devoted ourselves to the greatest possible development of the great Rocky Mountain area, or the Appalachian region. Then there is our great new state of Alaska— an empire whose potentials have not been touched, compared with its possibilities.

One could catalogue many other great opportunities that lie ahead.

But whether things happen in these and other aspects of American life in the next decade or two depends upon the utilization of our energies and the intensity of our interest in the further development of the people of the United States, as our first priority. It depends upon a conviction that the problems and opportunities in the regions of Denver and Newark

164

and Anchorage and Salt Lake City—for example—have "equal time," as the saying has it, with the problems of any other part of the world. It depends upon a conviction that the promotion of peace, the defense of the free world, and the defense of the concepts of freedom and of culture that are deep in our hearts must be made *first of all within our own country.*

A passion for developing to its fullest this underdeveloped country of ours in *every* way—human, physical, cultural, spiritual—is more crucial to peace, and fully as rewarding, challenging, and important to the destiny of all men everywhere, as anything we shall find in space or in the needy and remote and exotic parts of the world.

I have tried to give an outline—but only an outline—of what lies behind my conviction that hope *does* exist.

I find that hope not in any formula of world government, but of world community. This will come, I suggest, through a series of particular discrete acts, drawing closer together in economic and later in political unity, parts of our world where there is already the beginning of a common understanding. With all the occasional setbacks this is the way in which the increasingly closer bonds between the United States and Europe and the United States and the United Kingdom have come about in the past generation.

There are already strong ties of community between

countries that are not antagonists, countries that do not have nuclear weapons pointed at each other; the strengthening of these ties becomes, in my view, the first step in the far longer range objective of increasing a world-wide community of interest in which bit by bit the Soviet Union and its present satellites would begin to participate.

We can move toward the day when the terrifying dilemma of two great powers, the USA and the USSR, equipped with weapons capable of destroying the world, will no longer be so acute a threat; this will come about chiefly through a wide diversity of acts that have little or nothing *directly* to do with those weapons or any other weapons. The achievement of a world without war cannot, in my view, be accomplished except affirmatively by building up in a thousand different ways life-giving ties of common interest, first with those nations where such common interests already exist, and then little by little, case by case, between the Communists and the Free World.

It would be well at the outset not to be too ambitious and not to encourage too grandiose schemes, in order first to develop experience in working together, in directions that in time may bring the interests of the Soviet Union and the West closer together. This is not to say that Communism will renounce its aggressive goals, or that the West will recede from its belief in certain basic liberties and economic ideologies. But we can gradually remove from the center of the area of difference and discussion those dire atomic weapons, so that in time we find we are ameliorating the reasons why those weapons have any real bearing on living in a fluid, creative, changing world.

Such a long-range step-by-step program to reduce the terrible and very real risks of nuclear disaster will provide little comfort and no assurance to many of my fellow men. There will be many people who will find the slow diverse process of building a peaceful world quite unappealing and even intolerable while the risk of nuclear destruction hangs over their heads, over everyone's head. Some people will say that they simply cannot face life under the anxieties and tensions of the Atom while the changes I foresee have time to evolve and take effect.

To these I simply know no answer that will be both honest and satisfying. I do know that those who not long ago dug shelters and were preparing to live in them, or those few who ran away to some remote safe place to hide, soon found this to be a less tolerable way of existing than putting the potential danger out of mind. I believe that it is not how long one lives but the quality of life that counts, that sustains men. I do know that man is a most adaptive creature. And I do know that we are not the first generation of human beings who have had to live their whole lives face to face with mortal danger, whether of plague or constant warfare or the forces of nature; and I know too that it has often been those very periods, such as this one, when acute anxiety and danger of death were man's constant companions, that brought forth some of the most creative and robust chapters of history.

I believe in man. I believe he will not perish. Nor will the works of his spirit and brain and imagination vanish from the earth. I believe civilization will ride through this storm.

I do not believe that God created man and endowed him with the capacity to unlock the energy within the very heart of matter in order that he should use that knowledge to destroy this beautiful world, which is the handiwork not of man, but of God.